# MUM'S PUZZLE TIME

The name *Puzzler* is synonymous with enjoyable puzzles. *Puzzler* is the oldest and best known of all puzzle magazines, and the company is renowned for its puzzle expertise. As the largest puzzle publisher in the UK, and probably the world, Puzzler Media now publishes sixty titles in more than twenty countries.



This edition published in 2017 by Puzzler Media Ltd, Stonecroft, 69 Station Road, Redhill, Surrey RH1 1EY



A CIP catalogue for this book is available from the British Library.

ISBN 1-905346-90-3

Printed in the EU

**ACROSS**

1 Get even, take revenge (6,1,5)
8 Cry of a cat (5)
9 Flight company (7)
10 It is said, it is rumoured (3,5,4)
12 Fairy, elf (6)
14 1997 Robbie Williams ballad (6)
17 Broadcasting organisation (5,7)
21 Criminal's lever (7)
22 Colour of milk (5)
23 Self-government (12)

**DOWN**

1 House joined to another (4)
2 School tutor (7)
3 Leona ____, singer (5)
4 South American river (6)
5 Continue, keep going (5,2)
6 Horned African animal (5)
7 Keep trying (7)
11 Largest of all birds (7)
13 Problems, difficulties (7)
15 Inner feeling (7)
16 Go hungry (6)
18 Suffocate in water (5)
19 Dragged along behind (5)
20 Garden party (4)

# PUZZLE 2

## Ballet

| | | | | | | | | | | | | | | |
|---|---|---|---|---|---|---|---|---|---|---|---|---|---|---|
| G | K | E | T | E | J | W | X | H | E | I | G | C | R | U |
| I | R | B | A | L | L | E | T | T | H | I | C | R | T | G |
| X | I | M | N | B | R | E | N | I | H | N | O | U | C | R |
| I | U | B | O | L | A | I | P | D | R | A | T | O | E | L |
| G | P | E | N | V | O | L | M | U | S | D | S | K | E | O |
| R | I | D | D | P | E | I | A | H | O | E | A | L | A | W |
| H | R | A | N | E | C | M | O | N | K | C | E | N | D | L |
| S | O | N | S | R | D | E | E | A | C | V | A | O | C | I |
| T | U | E | N | P | S | S | L | N | A | E | T | A | H | E |
| R | E | M | S | O | M | N | A | T | T | I | U | L | A | T |
| G | T | O | M | A | A | U | I | P | P | S | O | B | S | C |
| D | T | R | N | W | R | O | J | H | L | S | N | I | S | O |
| T | E | P | S | E | N | V | A | L | I | N | R | R | E | E |
| I | S | G | L | I | S | S | A | D | E | O | U | A | T | E |
| C | D | E | R | R | A | B | L | R | G | N | T | M | I | S |

BALANCE
BALLET
BARRE
CHASSE
COUPE
DANCE
ELEVATION
GLISSADE
JETE
JUMPS
LEOTARD
MOVEMENTS
PAS DE DEUX
PIROUETTE
PLIE
POINTE
PROMENADE
SHOES
SWAN LAKE
TURN OUT
TUTU

# PUZZLE 3

## ACROSS

1 Hikers (8)
5 Toss (a coin) (4)
9 Lift, elevate (5)
10 Money saved for a rainy day (4,3)
11 Do as ordered (4)
12 ___ Barr, US actress (8)
14 Drivers' short cut (3,3)
15 Zone, area (6)
18 Amended, changed (8)
20 Extremely (4)
23 Amazing, wondrous (7)
24 Popular large house plant (5)
25 A doddle! (4)
26 Hit with a stick (8)

## DOWN

1 Trunk of the body (5)
2 Important, respected (7)
3 Was acquainted with (4)
4 Kidnapper's demand (6)
6 Sleep late (3,2)
7 Dog's dinner (4,3)
8 Directed (people) at a wedding (7)
13 Clumsy fool (7)
14 Poke around, ransack (7)
16 Thick sticky syrup (7)
17 Bring out of hiding (6)
19 Frock, gown (5)
21 Feel longing (for) (5)
22 Artificially coloured (4)

# PUZZLE 4

## Card Making

| | | | | | | | | | | | | | | |
|---|---|---|---|---|---|---|---|---|---|---|---|---|---|---|
| N | F | S | W | V | G | Q | A | O | G | A | N | O | A | N |
| O | O | A | T | L | T | D | N | N | A | O | T | F | R | A |
| N | O | B | U | E | C | D | I | R | T | A | E | L | E | G |
| N | K | E | B | M | N | S | O | R | U | L | E | R | T | R |
| T | I | A | I | I | S | C | S | R | E | K | C | I | T | S |
| S | E | R | W | O | R | N | I | U | E | C | D | L | I | R |
| C | T | A | B | O | I | T | G | L | E | N | A | R | L | E |
| I | O | M | D | E | C | O | U | P | A | G | E | I | G | T |
| S | E | L | F | T | D | A | P | K | N | I | M | F | E | S |
| S | V | A | S | O | B | E | C | D | N | R | U | M | I | E |
| O | O | E | W | P | I | T | E | V | S | A | P | R | L | Q |
| R | N | I | L | R | M | L | E | D | I | L | S | E | O | U |
| S | R | A | T | L | E | A | A | C | A | D | L | P | R | I |
| E | G | N | M | I | U | E | T | T | S | D | R | A | C | N |
| P | E | N | S | A | B | M | E | S | K | E | O | P | U | T |

BEADS
CARD
DECOUPAGE
EMBOSSING
FOIL
GLITTER
GLUE
INK PAD
PAPER
PENS
RIBBON
RULER
SCISSORS
SEQUIN
STAMPS
STENCIL
STICKERS
TEMPLATE
TRIM
VELLUM
WIRE

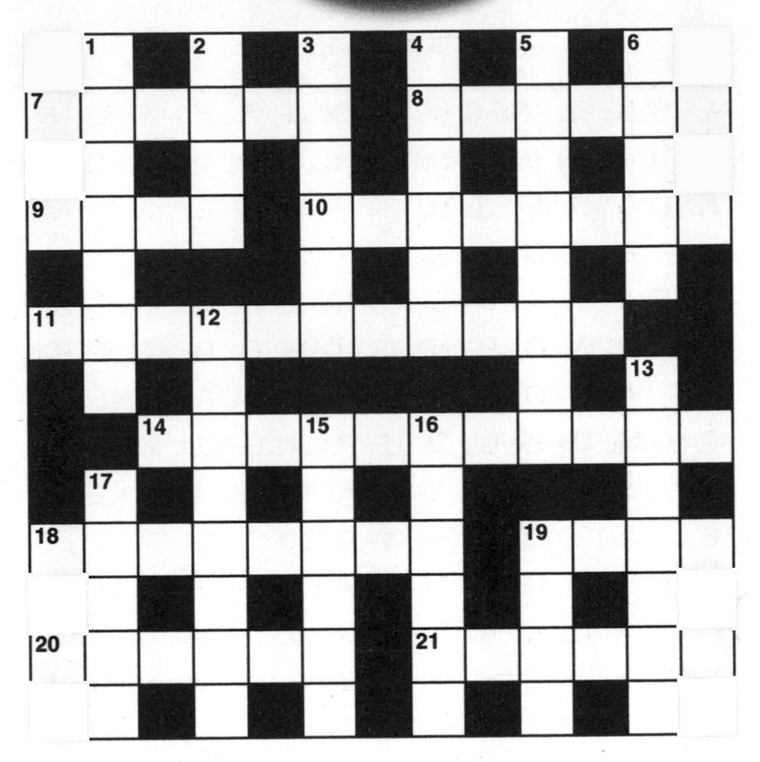


**ACROSS**

**7** Person starting a game in tennis (6)
**8** Connected to the internet (6)
**9** Zoom upwards (4)
**10** Decrease slowly (5,3)
**11** Support for workers on a building (11)
**14** Drive to ___, annoy intensely (11)
**18** Edible fungus (8)
**19** ___ evening, tonight (4)
**20** Tainted, unclean (6)
**21** Nakedness (6)

**DOWN**

**1** *Crazy in Love* singer (7)
**2** Finished (4)
**3** Santa's cave (6)
**4** Jumped on one foot (6)
**5** Reeded woodwind instrument (8)
**6** Make into one (5)
**12** Loyal, devoted (8)
**13** Club, association (7)
**15** Gardening hand tool (6)
**16** Variety of nut (6)
**17** Gin ___, card game (5)
**19** Sea movement (4)

# PUZZLE 6

## Crafts

| | | | | | | | | | | | | | | |
|---|---|---|---|---|---|---|---|---|---|---|---|---|---|---|
| L | S | G | D | G | S | L | B | Y | R | E | T | T | O | P |
| H | U | S | N | N | S | M | O | C | K | I | N | G | O | E |
| K | D | C | L | I | E | G | N | I | T | T | I | N | K | A |
| S | R | R | B | K | V | P | A | T | C | H | W | O | R | K |
| O | E | O | L | A | H | A | U | A | S | E | O | D | S | R |
| T | A | C | W | M | S | B | R | G | E | D | L | C | Q | M |
| A | S | H | O | D | R | K | N | G | E | A | I | E | U | H |
| P | G | E | B | R | O | I | E | C | N | M | U | G | I | G |
| E | N | T | E | A | H | O | O | T | A | E | N | D | L | N |
| S | I | L | S | C | T | U | W | R | R | I | R | A | T | I |
| T | T | O | T | E | P | I | E | A | V | Y | R | S | I | L |
| R | N | E | E | A | O | C | K | R | L | M | A | B | N | L |
| Y | I | E | G | N | I | K | A | M | E | C | A | L | G | I |
| D | A | E | R | H | S | C | U | S | E | W | I | N | G | U |
| O | P | E | P | V | T | I | E | D | Y | I | N | G | A | Q |

BASKETRY
BATIK
CARD-MAKING
CARVING
CERAMICS
CROCHET
DECOUPAGE
ENGRAVING
ETCHING
KNITTING
LACE-MAKING
PAINTING
PATCHWORK
POTTERY
QUILLING
QUILTING
SEWING
SMOCKING
TAPESTRY
TIE-DYING
WOODWORK

**ACROSS**

7 Bravery felt after alcohol (5,7)
8 Bite gently (6)
9 Mountain lions (5)
10 Track laps (8)
13 Mild cheese (4)
15 ___ Friel, English actress (4)
16 Blissful, divine (8)
17 Speak off the cuff (2-3)
19 Cause, motive (6)
21 Profitable business (5,7)

**DOWN**

1 Opposite of 'subtraction' (8)
2 Accidentally strike (your toe) (4)
3 Quiet because ashamed (8)
4 Broth (4)
5 First showing of a film (8)
6 A really long time (4)
11 Moving like a baby (8)
12 Esplanade (8)
14 From every side (3-5)
17 ___ bomb, nuclear weapon (4)
18 Part of a chair (4)
20 Sector, zone (4)

## Dances

| | | | | | | | | | | | | | | |
|---|---|---|---|---|---|---|---|---|---|---|---|---|---|---|
| O | F | O | X | T | R | O | T | H | G | K | W | G | Z | X |
| A | G | P | A | T | H | A | I | U | S | E | I | A | S | E |
| R | L | N | H | I | E | N | B | R | S | E | D | V | A | R |
| I | N | L | A | E | S | R | U | M | R | F | Q | O | D | I |
| E | H | U | E | T | E | M | N | A | A | U | S | T | A | E |
| Q | C | D | R | T | B | I | G | W | A | S | E | T | B | E |
| L | U | G | T | A | N | N | M | D | A | N | S | E | M | C |
| K | O | I | R | I | O | A | R | A | E | L | E | P | A | N |
| S | J | W | C | C | H | I | R | N | M | V | T | U | L | A |
| E | C | D | A | K | L | O | P | A | I | B | L | Z | R | D |
| S | O | I | T | L | S | E | N | J | T | R | O | D | S | N |
| A | E | O | E | I | L | T | T | G | F | E | C | I | D | R |
| L | N | R | H | S | U | I | E | O | T | E | P | S | V | A |
| S | L | N | R | H | O | R | N | P | I | P | E | C | E | B |
| A | I | S | O | O | C | N | E | M | A | L | F | O | T | E |

BARN DANCE
CONGA
DISCO
FLAMENCO
FOXTROT
GAVOTTE
HORNPIPE
JITTERBUG
JIVE
LAMBADA
MAMBO
POLKA
QUADRILLE
QUICKSTEP
RUMBA
SALSA
SAMBA
TANGO
TAP
TARANTELLA
WALTZ

**ACROSS**

1 From direct personal experience (2,5,4)
9 British armed service (5,3,5)
10 Creating, thinking up (8)
12 Guy, bloke (4)
14 Be nosey (5)
15 Woman whose husband has died (5)
19 On any occasion (4)
20 Most rapid, fastest (8)
22 Person returning to education (6,7)
24 League, club (11)

**DOWN**

2 Attempt (3)
3 Magic trick (8)
4 Very thin (6)
5 Sulking fit (4)
6 Arctic region's topmost point (5,4)
7 Vulgar, coarse (5)
8 Sobs (5)
11 Family feuds (9)
13 Reduction in price (8)
16 Bacteria (5)
17 Breakfast food (6)
18 Nation, country (5)
21 Musical threesome (4)
23 Self-importance (3)

# PUZZLE 10

## Embroidery Stitches

D M V M Z D M Y B L A N K E T
P D E R R O A L D R G M A P S
O T R A E O D F R A B E L H S
S L A Z Y D A I S Y G M O U O
O R T O N K N O I L L U B C R
I P B A C K J J S A T W E K C
G P E E N I L T U O W O Y U E
R N E N D F I L N S T V R A S
U O I I C T A K E H R E A R E
N S S H C R H E G E E N O I N
N I A H C C E I H S H W L T I
I G E T N U A T P S T H M A H
N S B E I R O L A E A E D R C
G S R U T N I C I N E E O T E
P F V S A T L R E I F L S O A

BACK
BLANKET
BULLION KNOT
CHAIN
CHINESE CROSS
COUCHING
FEATHER
FLY
FRENCH KNOT
HUCK
LAZY DAISY
OPEN CRETAN
OUTLINE
RUNNING
SATIN
SHEAF
SPLIT
STEM
STITCHES
STRAIGHT
WOVEN WHEEL

## ACROSS

**1** Raw mixed vegetables (5)
**4** Drug used by diabetics (7)
**8** ___ illusion, trick of sight (7)
**9** Rage (5)
**10** Facial hair on the forehead (7)
**12** Dance under a pole (5)
**14** Astronomer's place of work (11)
**18** Extent, scope (5)
**19** Full, satisfied (7)
**21** Easily creased cloth (5)
**23** Intended result (7)
**24** Christmas chocolate cake (4,3)
**25** Less dangerous (5)

## DOWN

**1** One who uses tobacco (6)
**2** Container for rubbish (6,3)
**3** Room's furnishing scheme (5)
**4** Poorly (3)
**5** Minor film actress (7)
**6** Limb used for walking (3)
**7** Having little width (6)
**11** Be indecisive (5)
**13** Ticked (items in a list) (6,3)
**15** Everlasting (7)
**16** Item used when it's raining (6)
**17** Bright, moving heavenly body (6)
**20** Capital of France (5)
**22** Zero score (3)
**23** Washing-line fastener (3)

# PUZZLE 12

## Gymnastics

| | | | | | | | | | | | | | | |
|---|---|---|---|---|---|---|---|---|---|---|---|---|---|---|
| B | F | H | E | E | E | H | E | E | D | G | E | F | E | H |
| E | S | E | D | E | L | G | N | S | O | I | E | P | L | H |
| A | N | Y | E | D | L | S | O | I | E | N | R | L | S | E |
| M | S | U | T | A | R | A | P | P | A | O | A | I | L | G |
| A | S | Y | M | M | E | T | R | I | C | B | A | R | S | A |
| G | F | P | A | T | T | N | U | O | M | S | I | D | C | E |
| N | C | C | R | D | L | E | A | P | S | N | R | R | Y | H |
| I | O | S | I | I | R | U | C | D | T | O | O | O | R | T |
| D | N | T | E | I | N | I | A | N | A | B | P | O | T | U |
| N | T | V | B | C | M | G | E | S | A | N | V | L | S | M |
| A | R | B | A | H | I | M | B | T | R | A | C | F | I | B |
| L | O | L | T | U | E | S | I | O | N | E | R | E | T | L |
| N | L | Y | E | V | L | C | U | I | A | S | M | O | R | I |
| A | H | T | O | Y | E | T | C | M | D | R | L | O | A | N |
| R | R | M | R | O | U | T | I | N | E | G | D | N | S | G |

ACROBATIC
APPARATUS
ARTISTRY
ASYMMETRIC BARS
BALL
BEAM
CONTROL
DANCE
DISMOUNT
FLOOR
LANDING
LEAPS
MOVEMENT
MUSIC
RHYTHMIC
RIBBON
ROUTINE
SOMERSAULT
SPRINGBOARD
TUMBLING
VAULT

**ACROSS**

**1** America's currency unit (6)
**4** Desert plant (6)
**9** Give money (3)
**10** Extremely inexpensive (4,5)
**11** Sculpt in wood (5)
**12** Pig's foot (7)
**14** After-dinner drink (5,6)
**17** Having no goal (7)
**18** Admit guilt (3,2)
**20** Startling event (3-6)
**22** Belonging to us (3)
**23** Hanging tuft of threads (6)
**24** Breakfast food (6)

**DOWN**

**1** Illustrate, show (6)
**2** Coating, tier (5)
**3** Person whose name is on an envelope (9)
**5** Curve (3)
**6** Supporting frame for a table (7)
**7** Extra good (5)
**8** Finding fault with (11)
**13** Away from the intended route (3,6)
**15** Baby's garment (7)
**16** Corkscrew shape (6)
**17** Watchful, wide awake (5)
**19** Not a soul (2-3)
**21** Baked pastry dish (3)

# PUZZLE 14

## Horse Competitions

| | | | | | | | | | | | | | | |
|---|---|---|---|---|---|---|---|---|---|---|---|---|---|---|
| G | B | O | W | V | F | T | J | G | I | B | I | Y | L | G |
| L | S | L | M | I | N | A | E | O | I | L | U | A | N | O |
| A | A | Y | R | T | I | A | U | E | B | E | L | H | K | G |
| S | D | M | R | E | I | N | S | L | M | N | M | S | C | K |
| U | D | P | T | N | I | O | P | O | T | T | N | I | O | P |
| F | L | I | O | R | T | E | I | E | A | S | E | N | L | E |
| E | E | C | P | W | N | Y | N | U | C | G | E | I | C | H |
| R | E | S | R | O | H | D | L | D | A | N | R | F | A | A |
| T | H | R | E | E | D | A | Y | S | U | O | A | R | S | I |
| S | T | S | E | N | T | A | S | R | E | R | D | L | O | I |
| H | T | L | C | R | T | E | G | M | A | H | A | B | A | E |
| O | C | N | A | O | R | D | N | R | A | I | H | N | U | B |
| W | I | C | E | D | R | O | T | T | R | E | P | V | C | A |
| S | K | L | N | V | R | E | S | T | E | I | S | O | A | E |
| S | T | Y | E | C | E | J | U | M | P | O | F | F | D | L |

BALANCE
CLOCK
DRESSAGE
ENDURANCE
EVENTS
FAULTS
FINISH
HARD HATS
HORSE
JUMP-OFF
MEET
OLYMPICS
POINT-TO-POINT
REFUSAL
REINS
SADDLE
SCORE
SHOWS
THREE DAYS
TRACKS
TRIALS

# PUZZLE 15

## ACROSS

**8** Version of a book (7)
**9** Willing, prepared (5)
**10** ___ Turner, Irish TV actor (5)
**11** ___ Day, Shrove Tuesday (7)
**12** Error in writing (4,2,3,3)
**16** Question (a witness) (5-7)
**20** Put on a costume (5,2)
**23** Complete, absolute (5)
**24** Habitual practice (5)
**25** Undo by twisting (7)

## DOWN

**1** Give back (money) (5)
**2** Very hot curry (8)
**3** Abduct for ransom (6)
**4** Quick cut (4)
**5** Late morning meal (6)
**6** Long detailed story (4)
**7** ___ Klass, TV presenter (7)
**13** Awkward situation (3)
**14** Hole in a bicycle tyre (8)
**15** Bread roll with a sugary glaze (4,3)
**17** Logical process (6)
**18** Hairstyling foam (6)
**19** Chestnut colour (5)
**21** Kian ___, former Westlife singer (4)
**22** Gush (4)

# PUZZLE 16

## Knitting

| | | | | | | | | | | | | | | |
|---|---|---|---|---|---|---|---|---|---|---|---|---|---|---|
| Y | H | W | V | J | H | P | A | A | B | H | A | Y | E | L |
| E | A | C | P | C | O | N | E | E | D | L | E | S | G | A |
| F | F | O | T | S | A | C | R | U | E | T | L | N | N | H |
| U | A | S | S | I | E | B | N | O | R | D | I | G | Y | E |
| R | A | C | N | B | T | D | L | A | E | T | O | L | A | G |
| L | G | O | O | S | O | S | H | E | T | R | O | R | R | D |
| R | A | U | I | E | P | C | G | I | A | W | F | U | N | E |
| H | Y | N | T | U | E | D | N | N | L | A | S | P | R | L |
| A | O | T | C | P | I | K | T | D | I | V | I | D | E | I |
| E | A | E | U | R | A | S | N | R | E | K | O | I | L | N |
| T | G | R | R | F | A | T | I | I | N | B | C | E | C | E |
| R | D | R | T | H | S | S | T | I | E | L | O | O | W | S |
| U | I | O | S | I | L | T | O | E | E | K | P | V | T | A |
| L | N | B | N | E | R | J | E | I | R | S | S | O | A | S |
| T | Y | E | I | C | D | L | R | G | N | N | I | S | A | K |

ANGORA
CABLE
CAST OFF
CHART
COUNTER
DIVIDE
EDGE
FAIR ISLE
INSTRUCTIONS
JOIN
KNITTING
LINES
NEEDLES
PATTERN
PURL
RIB
SKEIN
STOCKING STITCH
UNDO
WOOL
YARN

**ACROSS**

**8** Determine the heaviness of (5)
**9** Obvious, plain (7)
**10** Love affair (7)
**11** Dress in, clothe yourself in (3,2)
**12** Outgoing person (9)
**14** ___ Perkins, TV personality (3)
**15** Because, since (3)
**16** Legal term for unmarried women (9)
**19** Middle traffic light (5)
**21** Elected to power (5,2)
**23** Person who verifies something (7)
**24** Beat of blood in the wrist (5)

**DOWN**

**1** Change direction suddenly (6)
**2** Screen celebrity (4,4)
**3** At which time? (4)
**4** Blissfully calm (6)
**5** Arguments (8)
**6** In ___, as a joke (4)
**7** Immediately (2,4)
**13** Refusing to work as a protest (2,6)
**14** Quickly (8)
**15** Country, capital Paris (6)
**17** Turn upside down (6)
**18** Equipment for quick tanning (6)
**20** Make (tea) (4)
**22** Cassette (4)

# PUZZLE 18

## Line Dancing

| | | | | | | | | | | | | | | |
|---|---|---|---|---|---|---|---|---|---|---|---|---|---|---|
| G | J | U | C | O | A | S | T | E | R | S | T | E | P | S |
| S | T | O | O | B | Y | O | B | W | O | C | W | G | N | R |
| N | T | R | U | D | I | R | G | V | M | P | I | O | R | C |
| O | W | W | U | T | N | N | A | D | E | R | S | I | H | A |
| L | E | O | I | G | E | R | A | T | N | T | T | E | M | R |
| D | I | L | D | N | I | E | S | L | E | A | C | W | S | H |
| F | A | N | K | E | K | R | F | T | I | K | Y | E | T | K |
| A | U | P | T | C | O | L | S | Y | E | N | D | A | R | L |
| S | R | Y | P | L | U | H | E | D | C | A | E | V | I | A |
| H | I | N | I | L | A | B | S | S | R | N | I | E | K | W |
| I | G | A | M | F | E | H | T | A | T | B | A | S | S | L |
| O | S | D | N | R | I | J | H | L | U | E | E | F | G | E |
| N | A | M | E | R | I | C | A | N | E | V | P | I | N | M |
| E | E | O | T | L | E | E | H | C | O | B | O | A | O | A |
| D | L | S | S | P | U | R | S | M | K | N | R | I | L | C |

AMERICAN
APPLEJACK
BELT BUCKLE
CAMEL WALK
CHECKED SHIRTS
COASTER STEP
COWBOY BOOTS
FANCY FEET
HEEL TOE
HOEDOWN
IN A LINE
LONG SKIRTS
MOVES
OLD-FASHIONED
SAILOR STEP
SPURS
STETSONS
TWINKLE STEP
TWIST
VARIETY
WEAVE

# PUZZLE 19

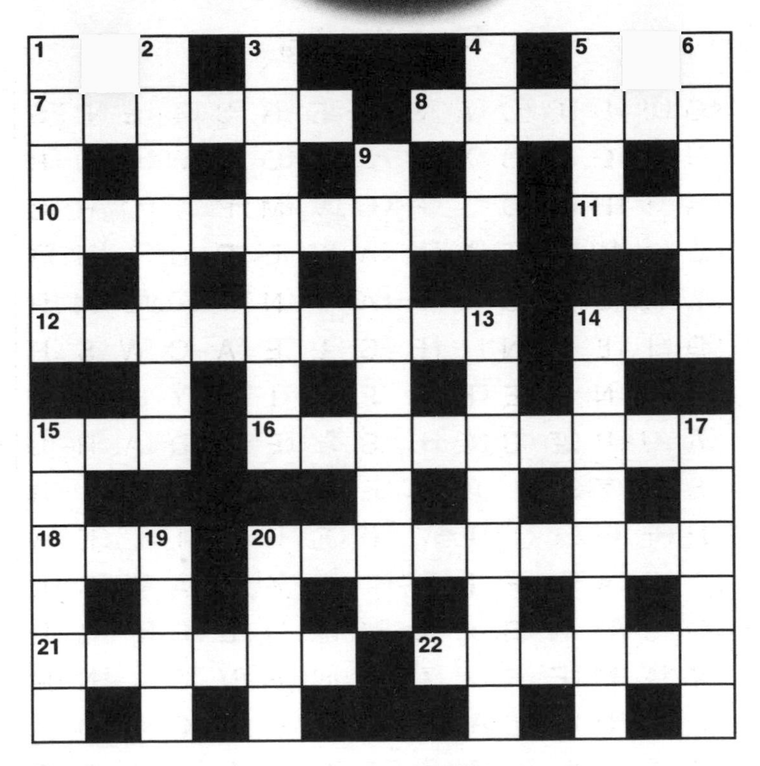

**ACROSS**

**7** One trying to lose weight (6)
**8** Condemned, ill-fated (6)
**10** Trading where goods are swapped (9)
**11** Nurses' employer (inits)(3)
**12** Going bang! (9)
**14** Paint container (3)
**15** Blue ___, small songbird (3)
**16** Have guests round (9)
**18** Carried out (an action) (3)
**20** ___ up, put into a package (9)
**21** Intact, total (6)
**22** Mean, miserly (6)

**DOWN**

**1** Can be eaten (6)
**2** Ramshackle, run-down (8)
**3** ___ Cruz, actress (8)
**4** Bad smell (4)
**5** Sign of future events (4)
**6** Better than evens, in betting (4-2)
**9** Clergymen (9)
**13** Items of clothing (8)
**14** Dragging behind (8)
**15** Put (a room) in order (6)
**17** ___ Hussain, *The Great British Bake Off* winner (6)
**19** Go out with (4)
**20** Wave (the hair) by using chemicals (4)

# PUZZLE 20

## Sunbathing

| | | | | | | | | | | | | | | |
|---|---|---|---|---|---|---|---|---|---|---|---|---|---|---|
| S | U | N | B | E | D | A | F | T | E | R | S | U | N | P |
| K | F | W | Z | E | C | N | A | T | S | I | S | E | R | D |
| P | I | N | E | D | L | O | G | D | E | E | D | E | A | P |
| E | L | A | E | C | O | D | B | T | I | K | A | E | K | T |
| R | T | T | I | A | I | E | B | R | C | P | G | W | S | E |
| E | E | C | A | D | L | R | R | O | O | N | A | B | U | O |
| S | R | S | I | N | O | T | L | E | I | W | T | I | N | T |
| S | A | R | I | N | N | B | S | T | E | O | N | L | S | I |
| U | L | M | Z | R | T | I | S | G | F | A | E | O | C | C |
| O | R | I | E | D | U | A | N | O | R | S | U | S | R | I |
| M | N | O | R | L | L | T | R | G | O | T | M | A | E | E |
| G | P | A | T | G | A | M | S | M | L | A | B | R | E | L |
| E | I | S | N | C | U | N | O | I | E | A | T | A | N | E |
| C | D | O | L | L | A | R | I | R | O | G | M | P | I | S |
| A | L | K | A | E | O | F | C | N | U | M | T | R | N | E |

AFTER-SUN
BALM
BLOCK
BRONZING
BROWN
CREAM
FACTOR
FILTER
FORMULA
GOLDEN
LONG-LASTING
MELANIN
MOISTURISER
MOUSSE
OIL
PARASOL
RESISTANCE
SUNBED
SUNSCREEN
TANNING
TINT

# PUZZLE 21

**ACROSS**

**8** Sleep all winter (9)
**9** ___ and bolt, fastener (3)
**10** Be ahead of (7)
**11** Small recess in a wall (5)
**12** Fib (3)
**14** In mint condition (5,3)
**17** Launder without water (3-5)
**19** Health resort (3)
**21** Similar (5)
**23** Authentic, real (7)
**26** Fireside carpet (3)
**27** Device for making things appear larger (9)

**DOWN**

**1** Having an attractive figure (7)
**2** Clever and competent (4)
**3** Needing no payment (4)
**4** Device for taking photographs (6)
**5** Body's blood carrier (4)
**6** Twists open (a jar) (8)
**7** Different, alternative (5)
**13** Jewellery worn on the lobes (8)
**14** TV and radio company (inits) (3)
**15** Great noise (3)
**16** Occupations, professions (7)
**18** Take on, employ (6)
**20** Become husband and wife (5)
**22** Jane Austen novel (4)
**24** Hard part of a finger (4)
**25** Flower or part of the eye (4)

# PUZZLE 22

## Yoga

| | | | | | | | | | | | | | | |
|---|---|---|---|---|---|---|---|---|---|---|---|---|---|---|
| A | U | H | B | A | L | A | N | C | E | A | H | T | A | H |
| F | M | W | A | Y | G | N | I | H | T | A | E | R | B | U |
| E | S | R | O | R | E | A | D | S | E | O | P | U | E | A |
| F | S | G | A | O | M | M | S | E | D | O | E | P | R | S |
| L | I | H | O | K | L | O | F | H | S | E | L | T | S | U |
| E | N | Y | C | A | N | S | N | T | T | T | N | I | E | Y |
| X | O | T | C | T | D | O | U | Y | C | A | D | R | B | P |
| I | E | I | L | D | E | R | I | A | M | D | N | G | C | A |
| B | N | L | S | K | E | R | P | T | H | O | R | G | H | R |
| I | E | I | P | W | N | M | T | A | A | U | E | C | A | E |
| L | L | G | S | R | I | O | S | S | E | T | N | R | K | H |
| I | S | A | E | W | O | A | I | L | G | F | I | M | R | T |
| T | B | E | O | C | N | D | N | R | S | U | I | D | A | O |
| Y | E | L | P | A | C | I | R | T | N | A | T | L | E | T |
| N | R | E | I | R | E | L | A | X | A | T | I | O | N | M |

AGILITY
ASHTANGA
BALANCE
BREATHING
CALM
CHAKRA
FLEXIBILITY
HARMONY
HATHA
KARMA
LOW-IMPACT
MANTRA
MAT
MEDITATION
POSTURE
RELAXATION
SIDDHASANA
STRETCH
TANTRIC
THERAPY
YOGI

## ACROSS

**8** ___ wand, Harry Potter's stick (5)
**9** Canvas bag (7)
**10** Girls' seven-a-side game (7)
**11** Very best, the cream (5)
**12** Decorated by sewing patterns (11)
**14** Older female relative (11)
**20** Examination of financial records (5)
**22** Announce openly or formally (7)
**23** Sweetheart (7)
**24** Be very good (at) (5)

## DOWN

**1** In the company of (5)
**2** Kitchen sandglass (3-5)
**3** Chocolate-covered cream cake (6)
**4** ___ con carne, spiced dish (6)
**5** Sheep's coat of wool (6)
**6** Hindu woman's garment (4)
**7** Collection of ships (5)
**13** Chic or gracefulness (8)
**15** Animal and plant life, eg (6)
**16** Present-day (6)
**17** Marked as correct (6)
**18** Country whose capital is Tokyo (5)
**19** Wobbly dessert (5)
**21** Female title equivalent to 'Sir' (4)

## Decorating

| | | | | | | | | | | | | | | |
|---|---|---|---|---|---|---|---|---|---|---|---|---|---|---|
| H | S | B | Y | G | K | S | H | A | D | B | H | W | T | U |
| V | A | L | L | Y | P | B | R | O | M | A | A | E | E | H |
| U | A | O | I | A | A | E | O | E | C | L | D | I | S | A |
| B | S | R | I | C | E | W | G | R | L | N | M | K | T | I |
| S | A | N | N | E | N | W | H | P | D | L | N | Y | E | T |
| R | T | U | E | I | C | E | A | D | A | E | O | O | R | A |
| O | I | P | T | E | S | P | T | N | A | R | R | R | P | O |
| T | E | A | E | M | E | H | C | S | R | U | O | L | O | C |
| A | S | T | O | R | I | G | M | A | B | E | C | G | T | R |
| R | D | T | D | E | S | I | G | N | E | R | N | N | S | E |
| O | R | E | I | S | T | I | P | P | L | I | N | G | V | D |
| C | H | R | U | L | T | I | O | K | V | T | E | A | I | N |
| E | L | N | N | T | E | R | E | O | L | I | O | A | N | U |
| D | T | S | A | Y | E | S | C | C | D | I | L | R | Y | G |
| N | M | M | N | O | I | S | L | U | M | E | S | I | L | S |

BORDER
COLOUR SCHEME
COVING
DECORATOR
DESIGNER
EMULSION
GLOSS
MATT
PAINT
PATTERNS
ROLLERS
SATINWOOD
SILK
STENCILS
STIPPLING
TESTER POTS
TILES
UNDERCOAT
VARNISH
VINYL
WALLPAPER

# PUZZLE 25

## ACROSS

**1** Sound of many voices talking at once (6)
**5** Dodged, bobbed (6)
**8** Notion, thought (4)
**9** Easy to get on with (8)
**10** Computer run-off (8)
**11** Plant that has bark (4)
**12** Traditional Lancashire dish (6)
**14** Knitted garment (6)
**16** Small restaurant (4)
**18** Museum's items on display (8)
**20** Temporary guests (8)
**21** Animal that butts (4)
**22** Win a victory over (6)
**23** Bingo's highest number (6)

## DOWN

**2** Be subjected to, suffer (7)
**3** Grey matter (5)
**4** Rounded protruberant sole section (4,2,3,4)
**5** Female star of *Fifty Shades of Grey* (6,7)
**6** Unit of a book (7)
**7** ___ Goulding, *Lights* singer (5)
**13** Accurate, exact (7)
**15** Competition participant (7)
**17** Girl who had adventures in Wonderland (5)
**19** Commenced (5)

# PUZZLE 26

## Ironing

| | | | | | | | | | | | | | | |
|---|---|---|---|---|---|---|---|---|---|---|---|---|---|---|
| S | Y | C | F | W | B | U | C | N | S | N | Y | H | B | U |
| R | D | I | I | O | T | I | N | T | H | Y | A | O | D | L |
| E | G | A | A | R | R | H | E | I | A | N | R | T | F | I |
| G | E | R | M | T | B | A | G | L | N | U | P | N | S | T |
| N | D | E | C | P | M | A | O | I | D | D | S | I | E | A |
| A | B | E | E | L | C | G | F | N | L | S | O | M | I | A |
| H | L | S | T | A | E | L | P | E | E | T | P | W | N | Y |
| E | U | P | G | E | C | H | O | R | E | E | O | D | L | S |
| A | O | R | N | I | E | S | R | T | R | N | A | L | S | E |
| O | I | E | I | L | T | E | M | A | H | G | M | F | I | A |
| B | E | S | H | C | R | D | T | O | N | S | U | I | O | P |
| T | E | S | S | I | N | U | S | L | O | R | T | N | O | C |
| A | L | U | A | N | R | O | E | I | S | T | C | O | R | D |
| O | A | R | W | E | T | Y | R | E | C | D | H | L | R | G |
| N | M | E | M | A | T | E | R | I | A | L | I | S | A | E |

AIRER
BOARD
CHORE
CONTROLS
CORD
DAMP CLOTH
ELECTRIC
FABRIC
HANDLE
HANGERS
HOT
IRON
MATERIAL
PILOT LIGHT
PLEATS
PRESSURE
SMOOTH
SPRAY
STEAM
TEMPERATURE
WASHING

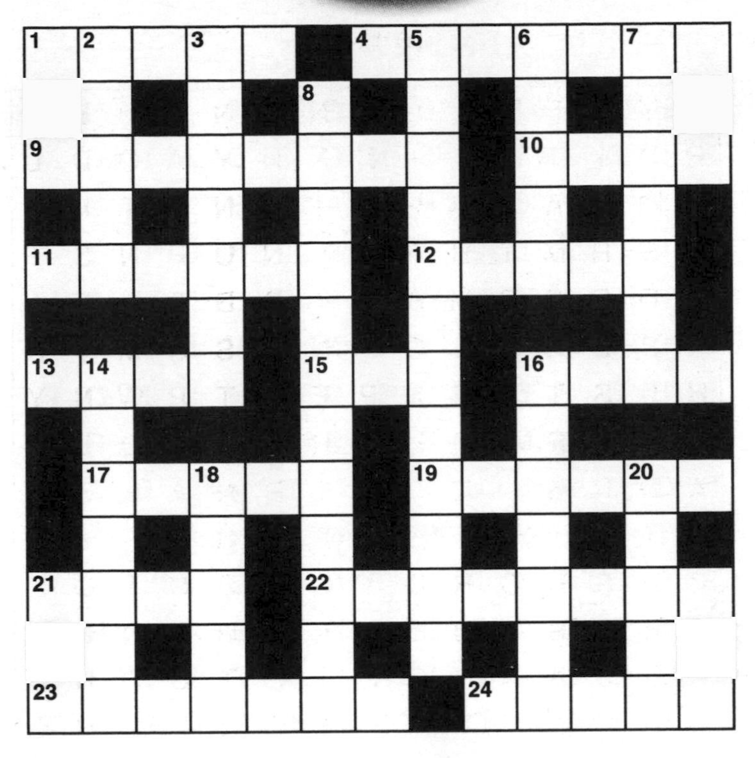

**ACROSS**

1 Make a hen noise (5)
4 Short-sleeved tops (1-6)
9 Relating to the arts (8)
10 Shine in the dark (4)
11 Small shellfish (6)
12 Causing death (5)
13 Dutch shoe (4)
15 Hurried along (3)
16 Bean used as a meat substitute (4)
17 Only just warm (5)
19 State, country (6)
21 Long hard journey, usually on foot (4)
22 Killed by the state (8)
23 Person who makes bouquets and wreaths (7)
24 Grading unit for gold (5)

**DOWN**

2 Chuckle (5)
3 Piece of a plant removed for propagation (7)
5 Done using your own money (4-8)
6 Bar of gold or other metal (5)
7 Shopping cart (7)
8 Readiness for action (12)
14 Word-for-word, exact (translation) (7)
16 Small sweet orange (7)
18 Gambling card game (5)
20 Drama set to music (5)

# PUZZLE 28

## Having A Bath

| | | | | | | | | | | | | | | |
|---|---|---|---|---|---|---|---|---|---|---|---|---|---|---|
| G | K | X | I | I | I | U | I | G | D | T | I | N | U | I |
| S | R | B | A | T | H | S | N | O | C | D | A | R | G | M |
| C | I | E | T | S | E | R | D | A | E | H | N | M | O | R |
| E | F | I | L | L | E | H | S | P | L | A | S | H | S | T |
| N | H | U | I | A | N | W | A | E | O | C | D | E | A | R |
| T | L | T | R | T | X | I | E | F | G | N | L | P | M | K |
| S | E | B | U | B | B | L | E | S | O | D | S | F | O | R |
| T | W | I | B | M | A | E | T | S | N | O | L | A | E | S |
| P | O | H | B | N | U | E | C | A | D | A | L | R | A | O |
| O | T | I | E | S | T | E | C | N | N | N | A | R | R | A |
| S | E | O | R | I | P | L | T | N | A | G | M | W | O | P |
| F | A | E | D | C | D | O | E | N | R | E | A | H | R | S |
| U | I | O | U | T | E | L | N | P | A | T | L | L | R | N |
| R | E | I | C | S | O | A | T | G | E | E | C | C | I | D |
| L | R | G | K | N | E | B | O | R | E | M | I | S | M | A |

BATH
BUBBLES
CANDLES
CLEAN
FLANNEL
HEAD REST
LOOFAH
MAT
MIRROR
RELAX
ROBE
RUBBER DUCK
SCENTS
SOAP
SPLASH
SPONGE
STEAM
TAPS
TILES
TOWEL
WATER

## ACROSS

**1** Angelic child (6)
**5** Garment worn by caterers (6)
**8** Canned fish (4)
**9** Car for short trips (8)
**10** Star sign, the Twins (6)
**11** Beautiful to look at (view) (6)
**12** Argument (4)
**14** ___ Hardy, actor (3)
**15** Metal percussion instrument (4)
**16** Luxurious variety of wool (6)
**18** Stop (a criminal) (6)
**20** Popular brew with a citrus flavour (5,3)
**22** Nation's emblem (4)
**23** Baby (6)
**24** Sewing device (6)

## DOWN

**2** Building to live in (5)
**3** Person accepting things as they are (7)
**4** Courtroom lawyer (9)
**5** Darken in the sun (3)
**6** Christians' holy book (5)
**7** Old friends' get-together (7)
**11** Repeat order (4,5)
**13** Radio programme with live callers (5-2)
**15** Long-necked creature (7)
**17** Perfume, fragrance (5)
**19** Garden pest in a shell (5)
**21** Shoddy goods (3)

# PUZZLE 30

## Dress Fitting

| | | | | | | | | | | | | | | |
|---|---|---|---|---|---|---|---|---|---|---|---|---|---|---|
| Y | T | W | V | Q | O | O | H | O | D | O | P | L | H | O |
| Y | D | A | L | B | E | M | P | I | R | E | L | I | N | E |
| R | D | M | O | O | U | R | F | L | H | O | E | D | R | W |
| E | C | A | A | C | L | T | N | A | L | G | A | R | A | N |
| M | S | I | R | M | I | S | T | K | O | R | T | I | A | W |
| B | E | H | R | T | N | T | Y | O | U | C | S | D | L | S |
| R | V | R | P | B | S | A | T | O | N | T | I | G | N | S |
| O | E | A | R | A | A | S | E | E | T | S | N | O | T | N |
| I | E | I | L | G | T | F | E | U | P | I | M | A | F | I |
| D | L | A | B | A | E | T | C | G | T | C | C | H | R | U |
| E | S | D | K | N | R | S | E | T | N | K | H | E | E | Q |
| R | S | E | U | I | A | O | U | R | I | A | E | M | T | E |
| Y | U | P | V | I | A | C | L | N | N | N | H | S | L | S |
| P | R | E | B | I | S | O | G | A | Y | E | E | C | A | C |
| D | F | I | T | T | I | N | G | S | E | L | D | E | E | N |

ALTER
BIAS CUT
BUTTONS
CHANGE
CUTTING
DARTS
EMBROIDERY
EMPIRE LINE
FABRIC
FITTING
HEMS
NEEDLES
PATTERNED
PETTICOAT
PLEATS
RAGLAN
SEQUINS
SLEEVES
TACKING
TAKE UP
WAIST

**ACROSS**

**1** Cloth strips or hair bands (7)
**5** Higher than (5)
**9** Outdoor-food relish? (8,5)
**10** Witch's cooking-pot (8)
**11** Close (4)
**12** Made more dense (9)
**16** Experiment, trial (4)
**17** Competed with (8)
**19** Impossible to rely on as honest (13)
**21** Smooth and glossy (5)
**22** General weather conditions (7)

**DOWN**

**2** To a certain extent, but not completely (2,1,3)
**3** Cap with a pompom at the top (6,3)
**4** More delightful (5)
**6** Bikini top (3)
**7** Clean by sucking up dust (6)
**8** Spiritualist's meeting (6)
**11** Caribbean percussion instrument (5,4)
**13** Stroke tenderly (6)
**14** Dog's shelter (6)
**15** Boiling to the touch (3-3)
**18** Letter that is not a consonant (5)
**20** Grass similar to wheat (3)

# PUZZLE 32

## Shopping

| | | | | | | | | | | | | | | |
|---|---|---|---|---|---|---|---|---|---|---|---|---|---|---|
| G | C | B | W | V | J | S | T | U | O | Y | A | D | I | N |
| I | O | N | I | G | E | N | P | D | I | M | O | N | E | Y |
| N | F | T | B | L | R | I | N | R | A | T | D | G | M | J |
| I | F | N | A | A | O | E | T | F | E | I | A | N | E | S |
| E | E | S | O | D | E | R | H | T | I | S | A | W | E | S |
| S | E | I | R | O | S | S | E | C | C | A | E | H | B | E |
| E | G | S | N | C | A | M | K | O | U | L | T | N | R | O |
| T | I | P | A | A | H | E | W | N | L | O | Y | U | T | H |
| E | D | O | L | R | C | R | A | E | L | O | V | C | I | S |
| L | T | H | E | P | R | N | R | C | A | M | R | A | E | O |
| E | U | S | I | A | U | Y | L | T | A | S | G | S | M | F |
| A | R | N | B | R | P | E | D | K | N | R | G | H | M | U |
| I | O | O | C | K | C | R | E | D | I | T | C | A | R | D |
| T | E | P | T | H | V | U | A | L | N | R | L | E | B | I |
| S | O | A | T | S | P | Y | E | D | L | L | L | L | I | T |

ACCESSORIES
BAGS
CAR PARK
CASH
CLOTHES
COFFEE
CREDIT CARD
DAY OUT
JEWELLERY
LUNCH
MAKE-UP
MALL
MONEY
PRESENTS
PURCHASE
SALES
SHOES
SHOPS
STORE
TILL
VOUCHER

**ACROSS**

1 Dead end (3-2-3)
6 Target in hockey (4)
8 Least in number (6)
9 High-calorie vegetable (6)
10 Acquire for money (8)
13 ___ McGregor, actor (4)
14 Little model (9)
17 Wild dog-like mammal (4)
18 Cutting indentations in (8)
19 Denoting women and girls (6)
21 Culmination, high point (6)
23 Shock into silence (4)
24 Person who grows plants (8)

**DOWN**

2 Medical term for 'womb' (6)
3 Stain (cloth) (3)
4 Location, surroundings (9)
5 Drinking vessel with a handle (3)
6 Hide out, lie low (2,2,5)
7 Off the right path (6)
11 Head of a clan (9)
12 Long-bodied family vehicle (6,3)
15 Humble, bashful (6)
16 Available in the shops (2,4)
20 Hen's produce (3)
22 Winter driving hazard (3)

# PUZZLE 34

## Washing Up

| | | | | | | | | | | | | | | |
|---|---|---|---|---|---|---|---|---|---|---|---|---|---|---|
| H | S | U | R | B | P | V | N | Q | P | A | S | T | A | N |
| O | A | T | C | O | L | D | W | A | T | E | R | U | E | Y |
| E | E | A | P | O | S | I | T | I | E | E | A | H | D | N |
| E | O | T | S | I | E | A | Q | E | L | L | C | N | O | S |
| T | I | A | C | E | V | P | H | U | N | T | C | Y | U | E |
| S | D | D | R | A | O | B | G | N | I | N | I | A | R | D |
| P | L | R | U | A | L | K | O | K | I | D | T | E | I | N |
| A | A | R | B | E | G | G | N | O | I | L | T | S | L | Y |
| T | A | E | B | R | R | R | S | I | C | D | H | E | N | R |
| L | R | H | I | S | E | E | U | O | S | W | W | I | C | E |
| O | L | N | N | T | B | A | E | P | A | O | V | A | L | K |
| L | S | I | G | N | B | S | R | S | T | K | E | I | O | C |
| E | S | O | W | A | U | E | H | A | T | Y | I | E | T | O |
| C | D | L | R | S | R | E | E | G | N | I | S | N | H | R |
| A | B | O | W | L | R | T | D | R | Y | I | N | G | G | C |

BOWL
BRUSH
CLEAN
CLOTH
COLD WATER
CROCKERY
DISHWASHER
DRAINING BOARD
DRYING
GREASE
KITCHEN
LIQUID
RINSE
RUBBER GLOVES
SCRUBBING
SINK
SOAKING
SUDS
SWILL
TAPS
TEA-TOWEL

## ACROSS

**1** Great operatic woman singer (4)
**4** Exciting detective story (8)
**8** Get by, muddle through (6)
**9** Exclusive set (6)
**10** High-fibre part of grain (4)
**11** Currents of air flowing through a room (8)
**13** 'Lady' in a seasonal stage show (9,4)
**16** Small rocky body orbiting the Sun (8)
**19** Onion-like vegetable (4)
**20** Drive or push forward (6)
**22** Line going from side to side (6)
**23** Perturbed, flustered (8)
**24** Rain heavily (4)

## DOWN

**2** Late with paying money that is owed (2,7)
**3** Not in favour of (7)
**4** Rough woollen cloth (5)
**5** Get back, recover (7)
**6** Being dishonest (5)
**7** Bird similar to an ostrich (3)
**12** Mild (climate) (9)
**14** Illuminated at night (7)
**15** Turkish ____, jelly-like sweet (7)
**17** Person now living and working abroad (5)
**18** Astounded, stunned (5)
**21** Old bit of cloth (3)

# PUZZLE 36

## Danielle Steel

B F U L L C I R C L E Y W J Z
U D D A A S G N I S S O R C B
U A Y N D N A P U A T G E B N
T F I G E H T A O H D N M I L
R T A B L S C N G O R I O G E
T T S A P C R I W N Y V H G A
U H E L I D S E L R A O G I P
S O E D E T O T M V E L N R O
R T E P S W S N A M N A I L F
E N H R R T E N I N U X O Z F
T X I E E O I J R M E S G O A
S F O R R S M E C H O E S Y I
I L C T H I M I R A C L E A T
S E A E B E N D S C I G A M H
S R D U O T E G P E V A L P N

ACCIDENT
BIG GIRL
CROSSINGS
ECHOES
FIRST SIGHT
FULL CIRCLE
GOING HOME
JEWELS
LEAP OF FAITH
LOVING
MAGIC
MIRACLE
PALOMINO
SECRETS
SISTERS
SUMMER'S END
THE GIFT
THE PROMISE
THE RING
VANISHED
ZOYA

**ACROSS**

**1** With a bathroom attached (2,5)
**5** Cigarette end (4)
**10** First, best (7)
**11** Drive off, push back (5)
**12** Large storage box (5)
**13** Man engaged to be married (6)
**15** Holiday centre (6)
**17** ___ McCartney, designer (6)
**19** Flashing line on a computer screen (6)
**20** Ongoing score (5)
**23** Walk in a leisurely way (5)
**24** Crusty white loaf (7)
**25** Mend (socks) (4)
**26** Half of 140 (7)

**DOWN**

**2** Sister's daughter (5)
**3** Bored and indifferent (12)
**4** Caution with money (6)
**6** Normal, average (7)
**7** Healing ointment (4)
**8** Ghost, phantom (7)
**9** Fairly slow way of swimming (12)
**14** All-in-one pyjamas for infants (7)
**16** Sleep (7)
**18** Increase threefold (6)
**21** Furthest point (5)
**22** Stiff paper (4)

## Jilly Cooper

O H B J U M P H T Y G N E T A
G C E H N D E K C I W E O P R
S N T T B E G N K O B R P T Y
E C I A L I T T L E M A B E L
R R O D V W H N L Y S U E L I
E I C R D I C L S S R O I I M
P V T L E E A E I N A E P S E
U A R S A T W O E O C A I A T
S L T G O S N S M N N A B A E
Y S E L C A S U E D D N R N I
L H O S T R U D O T I O T D R
L P E A E V U R A M A N R C R
O E I D S R A O A T Y K E O A
J C I D P L R I M O G E N G H
N R M N I H S U R S L E G N A

ANGELS RUSH IN
APPASSIONATA
BELLA
CLASS
EMILY
HARRIET
IMOGEN
JOLLY SUPER
JUMP
KATE'S WEDDING
LISA AND CO
LITTLE MABEL
MOUNT
OCTAVIA
PANDORA
POLO
PRUDENCE
RIDERS
RIVALS
SCORE
WICKED

## ACROSS

**1** Member of the legal profession (6)
**4** Handy and beneficial (6)
**9** Lean and bony (7)
**10** Seed of an oak tree (5)
**11** Boo, scoff (4)
**12** Embed surgically (7)
**14** Pay attention (6)
**16** Scribble aimlessly (6)
**19** Pipe-unblocking tool (7)
**21** Ode or sonnet, eg (4)
**23** Flat round foodstuff from Italy (5)
**24** Craving a drink (7)
**25** Badly torn (6)
**26** University qualification (6)

## DOWN

**1** Not as much (4)
**2** Networks of rabbit burrows (7)
**3** Full of enthusiasm (5)
**5** Hair cleanser (7)
**6** ___ and fauna, plants and animals (5)
**7** Increase (timespan, eg) (8)
**8** ___ Minogue, singer (5)
**13** Sticky stuff for catching insects (8)
**15** Cut into metal (7)
**17** Kitchen sideboard (7)
**18** Used a pen (5)
**20** Undo (a skirt or trousers) (5)
**21** Force with a lever (5)
**22** Extravagant publicity (4)

# PUZZLE 40

## Shakespeare's Women

F R O S A L I N D K J C U A T

T U T P S A O T F H L U C I S

O A L O I V R T B E E S M L S

K I O R T E A D O P I H O I B

K L A N D I U P N C E P D M E

A E S N V E A R N A H O A E A

T D H I A T S A B E S S T P T

H R L E R I R D L I S S O E R

A O N A L F C I E I A R A R I

R C S E O E A U R M T N T C C

I M F B E D N E L I O N C R E

N H S U O T N A A E P N V A N

E I S A B E L L A R E S A O T

E C D L R N M E N O I M R E H

S K A D N A R I M J U L I E T

BEATRICE
BIANCA
CASSANDRA
CLEOPATRA
CORDELIA
DESDEMONA
EMILIA
FRANCISCA
HELENA
HERMIONE
ISABELLA
JULIET
KATHARINE
LUCIANA
MIRANDA
NERISSA
OLIVIA
OPHELIA
PORTIA
ROSALIND
VIOLA

# PUZZLE 41

## ACROSS

1 Heavy filling food (6)
5 Truthful (6)
8 American version of 'pavement' (8)
9 Give out (radiation, eg) (4)
10 Purplish fruit (4)
11 Having a knees-up (8)
12 Town's outdoor trading area (11)
15 Pony meeting (8)
18 Large dinosaur (1,3)
20 System of relaxing exercise (4)
21 Vanishing-edge (swimming pool) (8)
22 Reprimand (6)
23 Untie, undo (6)

## DOWN

2 Spin (a baton) (5)
3 Person who needs to get real (7)
4 Typical specimen (7)
5 Cross-country walker (5)
6 Poverty-stricken (5)
7 Physics, biology etc (7)
12 Construction danced around in spring (7)
13 Full of fun (7)
14 ___ Banderas, actor (7)
16 ___ Reeves, actor (5)
17 Nimble, sprightly (5)
19 ___ Lauder, cosmetic brand (5)

# PUZZLE 42

## Alice In Wonderland

ALICE
CARDS
CATERPILLAR
CHESHIRE CAT
COURT
CROQUET
DINAH
DORMOUSE
DRINK ME
DUCHESS
EAT ME
FLAMINGO
KEY
KING
MAD HATTER
MARCH HARE
MOCK TURTLE
QUEEN
TEAPOT
WHITE RABBIT
WONDERLAND

| ■ | 1 | 2 |  | 3 |  | 4 |  | ■ | 5 | 6 |  | 7 |
|---|---|---|---|---|---|---|---|---|---|---|---|---|
| 8 | ■ |  | ■ |  | ■ |  | ■ | 9 | ■ |  | ■ |  |
| 10 |  |  |  |  | ■ | 11 |  |  |  |  |  |  |
|  | ■ | ■ | ■ |  | ■ |  | ■ |  | ■ |  | ■ |  |
| 12 |  | 13 |  |  |  |  | ■ | 14 |  |  |  | ■ |
|  | ■ |  | ■ | ■ | ■ |  | ■ |  | ■ |  | ■ | 15 |
| 16 |  |  |  | 17 |  | ■ | 18 |  |  |  |  |  |
|  | ■ |  | ■ |  | ■ | 19 | ■ | ■ | ■ |  | ■ |  |
| ■ | 20 |  |  |  | ■ | 21 |  | 22 |  |  |  |  |
| 23 | ■ |  | ■ |  | ■ |  | ■ |  | ■ | ■ | ■ |  |
| 24 |  |  |  |  |  |  | ■ | 25 |  | 26 |  |  |
|  | ■ |  | ■ |  | ■ |  | ■ |  | ■ |  | ■ |  |
| 27 |  |  |  | ■ | 28 |  |  |  |  |  |  | ■ |

## ACROSS

**1** Supermarket customer (7)
**5** Fifty per cent (4)
**10** Join a course (5)
**11** Short stiff hair (7)
**12** Getting on in years (7)
**14** Sheep's fleece (4)
**16** Tough-disciplined (6)
**18** Cooking in hot oil (6)
**20** ___ berry, palm fruit promoted as a 'superfood' (4)
**21** Shrill high-pitched cry (7)
**24** Small chocolate cake (7)
**25** Seaside residence (5)
**27** As well (4)
**28** Brighter (7)

## DOWN

**2** Belonging to the woman (3)
**3** Lighter in colour (5)
**4** Beginning of a baby (6)
**6** Officially allow (9)
**7** Run away (4)
**8** Set free (7)
**9** One who watches (6)
**13** Board members (9)
**15** Boffin, brainbox (7)
**17** Customer (6)
**19** Think well of, set a high value on (6)
**22** Thames or Severn, eg (5)
**23** *Mamma Mia* group (4)
**26** Tell an untruth (3)

## Cinderella

| | | | | | | | | | | | | | | |
|---|---|---|---|---|---|---|---|---|---|---|---|---|---|---|
| F | V | K | C | O | L | C | A | C | B | R | U | A | N | Y |
| C | E | M | N | O | I | T | A | T | I | V | N | I | E | S |
| I | G | L | A | S | S | S | L | I | P | P | E | R | M | R |
| N | R | E | A | G | T | O | R | F | E | C | U | A | T | E |
| D | S | E | O | L | I | R | A | B | I | E | S | O | O | T |
| E | S | P | E | L | L | C | R | M | A | E | H | N | O | S |
| R | E | H | T | O | M | D | O | G | Y | R | I | A | F | I |
| E | M | N | Y | S | T | E | P | M | O | T | H | E | R | S |
| L | U | I | E | E | D | D | C | S | L | R | P | A | O | Y |
| L | T | E | D | H | A | E | N | N | L | A | U | R | S | L |
| A | P | R | I | N | C | E | C | H | A | R | M | I | N | G |
| E | O | T | D | A | I | T | G | F | B | D | P | A | B | U |
| E | D | I | L | N | R | G | I | H | S | U | K | O | T | E |
| V | N | A | A | N | R | E | H | K | S | O | I | A | T | Y |
| I | P | E | D | S | N | O | T | T | U | B | N | L | R | G |

BALL
BUTTONS
CASTLE
CINDERELLA
CLOCK
DANCE
DANDINI
FAIRY GODMOTHER
FOOTMEN
GLASS SLIPPER
INVITATION
KITCHEN
MAGIC
MICE
MIDNIGHT
PALACE
PRINCE CHARMING
PUMPKIN
SPELL
STEPMOTHER
UGLY SISTERS

## ACROSS

**7** Astonishing or impressive (7)
**9** Grown-up (5)
**10** Belonging to us (3)
**11** Care for, tend (4,5)
**12** Cookery clothing (5)
**14** Wing of a dolphin (7)
**16** Someone who gives you hints and tips (7)
**18** Ask God's protection for (5)
**19** Face the opposite direction (4,5)
**20** ___ Direction, boy band (3)
**21** Swallowed liquid (5)
**22** Stylish, graceful (7)

## DOWN

**1** View of a wide area (8)
**2** Travelling amusement arcade (4)
**3** Instrument played under the chin (6)
**4** Highly seasoned Italian sausage (6)
**5** Of many parts (8)
**6** Mix with a spoon (4)
**8** Happy chance, luck (4,7)
**13** Backward movement (8)
**15** Has admiration for (8)
**17** Caress, pet (an animal) (6)
**18** Organise your finances (6)
**19** Sea movement (4)
**20** Milky-coloured precious stone (4)

# PUZZLE 46

## Snow White

H U N T S M A N B K V Z B U N
D Y E L P P A D E N O S I O P
T L P I Y H A S N C O I L U N
S E O M A P E N C O Q Q F D R
E R G P U G E E I D S A I O B
R T P L A R E E L M I E R S G
I Y I T A N G Z L R A R V T K
A D T H O S R Y Y S I L T E I
F O A E W H S T N M U E S P N
C P C D L W A C C R A O D M E
I E T E N L O I A A R W E O C
O Y I L E T G N G S A A B T N
L U F H S A B E S R K C D H I
N R H U M I O T F E V E A E R
F O R E S T L S N R E I T R P

ANIMALS
BASHFUL
COTTAGE
DOC
DOPEY
DWARFS
FAIREST
FAIRYTALE
FOREST
GLASS CASKET
GRUMPY
HAPPY
HUNTSMAN
MAGIC MIRROR
POISONED APPLE
PRINCE
SEVEN
SLEEPY
SNEEZY
SNOW WHITE
STEPMOTHER

# PUZZLE 47

| | 1 | | 2 | | 3 | | 4 | | 5 | | 6 | |
|---|---|---|---|---|---|---|---|---|---|---|---|---|
| 7 | | | | | | | | | 8 | | | |
| | | | | | | | | | | | | |
| 9 | | | | | | | 10 | | | | | |
| | | | | | | | | | | | | |
| 11 | | | | | 12 | | | | 13 | | | |
| | | | | | | | | | | | | |
| 14 | 15 | | | | 16 | | 17 | | 18 | | 19 | |
| | | | | | | | | | | | | |
| | 20 | | 21 | | | | 22 | | | | | |
| | | | | | | | | | | | | |
| 23 | | | | | 24 | | | | | | | |
| | | | | | | | | | | | | |

**ACROSS**

**7** Ate in a restaurant (5,3)
**8** Uncommon (4)
**9** Be unable to make a decision (6)
**10** Pour fat over (roasting meat) (5)
**11** Oven for baking pottery (4)
**12** Mon to Fri! (8)
**14** Cafe for a light meal (5,3)
**18** Robe, dress (4)
**20** Stretch (your neck) to see better (5)
**22** Sponge, custard and cream pudding (6)
**23** Hindmost part of an animal (4)
**24** Rained for a short while (8)

**DOWN**

**1** Skimpy two-piece swimsuit (6)
**2** Person who repairs cars (8)
**3** Obtain on loan (6)
**4** Shelter for horses (6)
**5** Coloured part of the eye (4)
**6** Body's blood vessel (6)
**13** Completely exhausted (3-5)
**15** Flower liquid collected by bees (6)
**16** Piece of chicken (6)
**17** Allotted amount (6)
**19** Travelled on foot (6)
**21** Friend during a conflict (4)

# PUZZLE 48

## Female Singers

ALISON MOYET
ANASTACIA
BEYONCE
BILLIE
BJORK
CHER
ENYA
GABRIELLE
JAMELIA
JAVINE
JOSS STONE
KATE BUSH
KATIE MELUA
KELIS
LILY ALLEN
LULU
PINK
SHAKIRA
TIFFANY
TOYAH
YAZZ

# PUZZLE 49

## ACROSS

**7** Laughs furtively (8)
**8** ___ pudding, stodgy dessert (4)
**9** Upper part of a dress (6)
**10** Occurring annually (6)
**11** Have a try at (7)
**13** Child's toy bear (5)
**15** Quick wash (5)
**17** Organised campaign for reform (7)
**19** Event that will never happen again (3-3)
**21** Hair falling over the brow (6)
**23** Or ___, otherwise (4)
**24** Without telling anybody (8)

## DOWN

**1** Release (a knot) (4)
**2** Set fire to (something) (6)
**3** Proof that a bill is paid (7)
**4** Children's 'spotting' game (1-3)
**5** ___ agent, seller of property (6)
**6** Quiet and sheltered from view (8)
**12** Three-sided figure (8)
**14** Responsible school pupil (7)
**16** Taken illegally (6)
**18** Web-making creature (6)
**20** Bustle, commotion (4)
**22** Jamboree (4)

## Girl Bands

| | | | | | | | | | | | | | | |
|---|---|---|---|---|---|---|---|---|---|---|---|---|---|---|
| K | S | X | M | C | Q | N | D | A | C | D | D | O | L | T |
| W | O | L | L | I | R | S | L | C | U | D | O | O | A | H |
| C | I | O | R | U | S | L | E | O | D | B | A | K | N | R |
| S | U | L | B | I | S | T | L | L | E | O | M | W | R | E |
| T | E | P | S | A | G | A | E | L | G | E | A | H | E | E |
| N | E | M | I | O | S | E | L | E | U | N | R | C | T | D |
| H | H | N | E | L | N | E | C | G | Q | D | A | R | E | E |
| O | T | E | R | R | S | P | O | I | N | R | N | B | R | G |
| S | O | I | A | T | P | V | H | I | P | M | A | A | O | R |
| W | G | C | A | R | N | U | D | I | N | S | N | R | N | E |
| V | H | R | U | E | T | I | S | O | L | P | A | V | E | E |
| A | S | U | G | A | B | A | B | E | S | L | B | N | T | S |
| X | I | M | E | L | T | T | I | L | R | I | I | O | T | A |
| S | H | A | N | G | R | I | L | A | S | T | E | P | E | C |
| D | N | E | T | T | I | K | C | I | M | O | T | A | S | R |

ALL SAINTS
ATOMIC KITTEN
BANANARAMA
BANGLES
BELLE STARS
CLOUT
EN VOGUE
ETERNAL
GIRLS ALOUD
HEART
HEPBURN
LITTLE MIX
MIS-TEEQ
RONETTES
SHANGRI-LAS
SPICE GIRLS
SUGABABES
SUPREMES
SWV
THREE DEGREES
WILSON PHILLIPS

# PUZZLE 51

**ACROSS**

**1** Intelligent African ape (10)
**8** Physical dimensions (5)
**9** Climbing shoot of a plant (7)
**10** Dried grape (7)
**11** Be alive (5)
**12** Protectors, keepers (9)
**15** Breakfast food (5)
**17** Back a car (7)
**19** Boastfully try to impress (4,3)
**20** Book of fiction (5)
**21** Entered in an official list (10)

**DOWN**

**2** Light-brown nut (5)
**3** Eyelash make-up (7)
**4** Creative, practical pursuits (4,3,6)
**5** Greek isle, also called Zakinthos (5)
**6** Common garden insects (7)
**7** Apartment (4)
**8** Band worn over the shoulder (4)
**12** Attractiveness that suggests wealth (7)
**13** Go forward (7)
**14** In good health (4)
**15** Job to be performed (4)
**16** G-string (5)
**18** Theatrical production consisting of unrelated sketches (5)

## PUZZLE 52

### Kylie Songs

```
T V N W O D O C S I D E J P S
N H A E S D K I D S K M N A H
G N E L H R R F A R P N U A O
N R O L E T R E A A B I L G C
S W E V O A A D A N T E I L K
E A E D G C R E C M P D R I E
S F L I N E O H R W S I N N D
I U L I T E O M C B G F L Y S
M E A F M C R I O S T N E O N
O A A S O B E R I T I O L U T
R G A L B E O H U P I C C R N
P H A S U I T T E S M O P E V
A T T O O F A R L N R U N Y E
E Y L F R E T T U B I S J E A
T L I G H T Y E A R S Y E S C
```

AFTER DARK
BREATHE
BUTTERFLY
CHOCOLATE
CONFIDE IN ME
DISCO DOWN
DREAMS
FEVER
FRAGILE
IN YOUR EYES
JUMP
KIDS
LIGHT YEARS
LIMBO
PROMISES
SHOCKED
SLOW
SURRENDER
THE LOCOMOTION
THIS GIRL
TOO FAR

## ACROSS

1 Mixing spoon (7)
5 Adjust (a clock) (5)
8 Person representing an actor (5)
9 Body rub (7)
10 ___ lady, road-crossing helper (8)
11 Delicate expensive fabric (4)
13 Traveller's receipt (6)
15 Keep-fit runner (6)
18 Pull along the ground (4)
19 Glasgow's country (8)
22 ___ balls, pungent sweets (7)
23 Go for a swim (5)
24 Time when we sleep (5)
25 Closely cropped hairstyle (4,3)

## DOWN

1 Poppy colour (7)
2 Absolutely perfect (5)
3 Shopkeeper (8)
4 Light-hearted love film (6)
5 Flower with thorns (4)
6 Using a razor (7)
7 Sharp pinch (5)
12 Easily moved about (8)
14 Strong desire or an intense longing (7)
16 Food such as beef and lamb (3,4)
17 Sour-tasting (6)
18 Sewage pipe (5)
20 Space within the top of a house (5)
21 Come face to face with (4)

## Madonna Songs

| | | | | | | | | | | | | | | |
|---|---|---|---|---|---|---|---|---|---|---|---|---|---|---|
| C | F | J | Z | L | L | N | N | P | N | T | W | N | T | C |
| H | N | P | O | Y | I | L | T | F | N | H | S | P | H | E |
| E | O | C | R | D | T | K | E | C | I | S | U | M | O | M |
| R | R | R | N | S | O | E | E | T | T | U | I | A | L | E |
| I | O | A | P | T | U | W | E | A | O | P | S | H | I | U |
| S | E | N | T | G | A | H | U | Y | V | T | C | D | D | C |
| H | N | E | O | S | E | K | S | S | A | I | E | A | A | S |
| O | I | V | I | A | Y | S | E | Y | T | N | R | V | Y | E |
| A | L | E | T | S | E | K | O | A | A | I | L | G | I | R |
| T | R | R | G | R | M | F | C | M | B | A | B | C | I | L |
| D | E | Y | D | N | H | S | A | U | U | O | I | O | T | N |
| E | D | B | F | R | O | Z | E | N | L | P | W | A | L | N |
| R | R | O | L | R | I | G | L | A | I | R | E | T | A | M |
| E | O | D | I | N | R | E | L | B | M | A | G | S | O | A |
| T | B | Y | G | E | D | E | A | R | J | E | S | S | I | E |

AMAZING
BORDERLINE
CHERISH
DEAR JESSIE
DRESS YOU UP
EVERYBODY
FROZEN
GAMBLER
HOLIDAY
LIKE A VIRGIN
LIVE TO TELL
LUCKY STAR
MATERIAL GIRL
MUSIC
PUSH
RESCUE ME
SORRY
STAY
TAKE A BOW
VOGUE
WHITE HEAT

**ACROSS**

**1** Garden bloom (7,5)
**8** Edition (of a magazine etc) (5)
**9** Existing in the physical world, not artificial (7)
**10** Knobbly leg joint (4)
**11** Bouquet makers (8)
**14** Abrupt, unexpected (6)
**15** Dull, boring (6)
**17** Commonplace, usual (8)
**18** Crush food between the teeth (4)
**21** Sheltered hot spot (7)
**23** Paved garden area (5)
**24** Joining up again (12)

**DOWN**

**1** Flicker the eyes (5)
**2** Moved downwards (9)
**3** Chilled (tea, eg) (4)
**4** Mild, kind (6)
**5** Concerning books and writing (8)
**6** Word paired with 'neither' (3)
**7** Elegant, sophisticated (6)
**12** Stringy variety of pasta (9)
**13** ___ DiCaprio, actor (8)
**14** Husband or wife (6)
**16** Call and pay a short visit (4,2)
**19** Not right (5)
**20** Heroic tale (4)
**22** Born as (3)

# PUZZLE 56

## Anniversaries

| | | | | | | | | | | | | | | |
|---|---|---|---|---|---|---|---|---|---|---|---|---|---|---|
| U | S | T | E | E | L | G | W | Z | E | S | U | G | M | S |
| I | C | W | N | S | T | B | H | U | Z | I | N | S | L | C |
| T | G | O | N | I | T | M | D | I | N | N | E | A | Y | H |
| A | S | O | R | T | I | L | E | H | O | N | C | R | U | I |
| A | N | D | S | A | O | E | O | D | R | E | O | T | X | N |
| X | D | I | A | G | L | B | E | G | B | V | N | R | M | A |
| S | C | I | R | S | A | P | P | H | I | R | E | O | I | R |
| T | R | I | A | E | N | O | T | T | O | C | A | E | D | E |
| W | Y | H | N | M | H | Y | U | E | C | D | L | L | S | P |
| A | S | O | I | T | O | T | E | N | A | R | A | S | S | P |
| E | T | O | R | I | L | N | A | T | G | R | M | I | A | O |
| B | A | E | C | E | D | N | D | E | E | R | L | H | S | C |
| U | L | I | O | T | P | E | V | M | L | V | A | L | N | R |
| E | I | S | O | A | T | A | E | Y | E | E | C | D | L | R |
| G | L | R | A | E | P | N | P | R | M | I | R | U | B | Y |

BRONZE
CHINA
COPPER
CORAL
COTTON
CRYSTAL
DIAMOND
EMERALD
GOLD
IRON
IVORY
LACE
LEATHER
PAPER
PEARL
RUBY
SAPPHIRE
SILVER
STEEL
TIN
WOOD

## ACROSS

**1** Daily record of events (7)
**5** Front of the head (4)
**8** Light purple colour (5)
**9** Vote for neither side (7)
**11** As the ___ flies, in a straight line (4)
**12** Lacking courage (8)
**15** At no time (5)
**16** Entice, lure (5)
**19** Teach, educate (8)
**21** Exhale with relief (4)
**23** Liberty (7)
**25** Panic button (5)
**26** At this place (4)
**27** Tittered (7)

## DOWN

**2** Bystanders (9)
**3** Toast holder (4)
**4** South American river (6)
**5** Grease (3)
**6** Make cold (5)
**7** Time-teller (5)
**10** Looked fixedly (6)
**13** Exact copy (9)
**14** Rose up on the hind legs (6)
**17** Large prawns in breadcrumbs (6)
**18** ___ park, outdoor amusement complex (5)
**20** Care for sick people (5)
**22** Explosive noise (4)
**24** Female sheep (3)

# PUZZLE 58

## Arthurian Times

| | | | | | | | | | | | | | | |
|---|---|---|---|---|---|---|---|---|---|---|---|---|---|---|
| D | K | E | W | T | E | L | T | S | A | C | J | S | O | D |
| A | S | O | S | B | E | S | O | B | M | E | R | L | I | N |
| H | T | Y | D | R | D | R | E | M | S | O | T | F | T | G |
| A | L | E | S | L | O | D | R | E | O | D | T | I | R | U |
| L | B | I | E | E | I | H | T | U | M | S | K | O | U | I |
| A | T | I | A | V | J | O | U | S | T | I | N | G | O | N |
| G | H | I | E | M | L | F | E | W | N | Y | A | U | C | E |
| S | E | R | D | E | N | S | A | R | F | W | O | I | T | V |
| T | E | E | M | A | N | I | R | L | A | L | S | E | H | E |
| B | O | A | I | T | R | G | A | I | C | M | A | F | G | R |
| A | C | B | E | C | D | T | N | H | N | O | R | G | I | E |
| N | Y | R | L | A | V | I | H | C | C | H | N | S | N | U |
| N | I | O | T | E | A | L | N | U | R | E | I | R | K | S |
| E | O | A | T | Y | E | H | C | D | R | L | R | G | Y | N |
| R | M | L | A | N | C | E | S | I | N | O | L | A | V | A |

ARTHUR
AVALON
BANNER
BEDIVERE
CAMELOT
CASTLE
CHAIN MAIL
CHIVALRY
COURT
FALCONRY
FLAG
GALAHAD
GAWAIN
GUINEVERE
HORSE
JOUSTING
KNIGHT
LANCES
MERLIN
SHIELD
TURRET

**ACROSS**

1 Mollycoddle (6)
4 Put the ball into play at tennis (6)
8 Running for fun (7)
10 Beauty parlour (5)
11 Perhaps (5)
12 Besides, at all events (6)
13 Opposite of 'rough' (6)
15 Deliberately avoid (6)
19 Cows (6)
21 Changed your address (5)
24 (Had) started (5)
25 Mid-afternoon refreshment period (7)
26 More simple (6)
27 Put emphasis on (6)

**DOWN**

1 Nightclothes (7)
2 Clammy (weather) (5)
3 Important, respected (7)
5 School composition (5)
6 Mountain emitting lava and gas (7)
7 Coastal sandhill (4)
9 Metric unit of weight (4)
14 Citrus fruits (7)
16 Acrobatic athlete (7)
17 Constant, unceasing (7)
18 Of the highest quality (4)
20 Anxious (5)
22 Means of speech (5)
23 Skilled and talented (4)

# PUZZLE 60

## Bags

| | | | | | | | | | | | | | | |
|---|---|---|---|---|---|---|---|---|---|---|---|---|---|---|
| C | R | E | P | M | A | H | G | M | F | W | V | D | N | N |
| A | M | O | D | I | N | A | N | O | T | E | C | A | S | E |
| R | P | O | I | N | B | O | E | D | L | M | I | N | E | O |
| R | I | T | R | D | K | T | X | O | B | H | C | N | U | L |
| I | R | F | N | E | R | I | I | E | L | N | S | E | S | O |
| E | G | A | D | U | S | S | T | K | R | T | I | U | G | E |
| R | H | L | N | N | A | A | C | B | M | S | I | H | A | O |
| R | R | K | T | T | I | A | C | E | A | T | W | A | B | H |
| E | N | U | C | T | P | E | D | F | C | G | G | T | T | O |
| S | L | H | C | K | E | S | Z | A | E | A | Z | B | E | L |
| I | E | R | C | K | O | K | S | I | W | I | T | O | P | D |
| L | E | A | N | R | S | E | S | S | S | E | R | X | R | A |
| A | B | O | I | L | T | A | M | A | F | E | D | B | A | L |
| V | N | R | S | U | I | O | C | T | B | E | P | V | C | L |
| L | L | U | G | G | A | G | E | K | N | P | O | U | C | H |

BACKPACK
BASKET
BRIEFCASE
CARPET BAG
CARRIER
GRIP
HAMPER
HANDBAG
HATBOX
HOLDALL
KITBAG
LUGGAGE
LUNCH BOX
NOTECASE
POUCH
RUCKSACK
SATCHEL
SUITCASE
SWAG
TRUNK
VALISE

## ACROSS

1 Visited by ghosts (7)
5 Do as you're told (4)
9 Cover put over curlers (7)
10 Dizzy (5)
11 Take possession of (territory) (5)
12 Alternative name for a puma (6)
14 Stand firm against (6)
16 French-style cafe (6)
18 In the very near past (6)
19 Tell off (5)
22 Oust from a dwelling (5)
23 Act of saying 'sorry' (7)
24 Shopper's memory aid (4)
25 Reacted to pepper? (7)

## DOWN

2 Visitor from space (5)
3 Imaginary, unreal (3-8)
4 Coax, tempt (6)
6 Skin tattoo or design (4,3)
7 Child's toy on a string (2-2)
8 Building with a stage and seats (7)
10 Be destroyed by fire (2,2,2,5)
13 Farewell (7)
15 Variety of animal etc (7)
17 Pour through a colander (6)
20 Threatened atmospheric layer (5)
21 Exchange for cash (4)

# PUZZLE 62

## Clothes Beginning C

CAMISOLE
CAPE
CAPRI PANTS
CARDIGAN
CHEMISE
CHINOS
CLOAK
CLOCHE HAT
CLOGS
COAT
COLLAR
CONTROL PANTS
CORONET
CORSET
COSTUME
COURT SHOES
COWBOY HAT
CRINOLINE
CROP TOP
CUFFS
CULOTTES

# PUZZLE 63

**ACROSS**

**8** Divided into four equal parts (9)
**9** Animal very like a human (3)
**10** Collection of public records (7)
**11** Distribute in portions (5)
**12** Nearest and dearest (3)
**14** Overturning (2-6)
**16** Cocoons, wraps up (8)
**18** Common dog command (3)
**21** Clumsy, bungling (5)
**23** Insulated container (4,3)
**25** ___ Angeles, US city (3)
**26** Not on the guest list (9)

**DOWN**

**1** Parrot's croaky call (6)
**2** Bathroom powder (4)
**3** State of mind, disposition (8)
**4** Horizontal wall decoration (6)
**5** Thought (4)
**6** Trees-to-be (8)
**7** Dentures (5)
**13** Rubbish (8)
**15** Break down in water (8)
**17** Exotic flower (6)
**19** Dinner jacket (6)
**20** Church walkway (5)
**22** Accurate, genuine (4)
**24** Washtub (4)

# PUZZLE 64

## Clothes Beginning S

SANDALS
SARI
SARONG
SASH
SCARF
SHAWL
SHORTS
SKIRT
SLACKS
SLINGBACKS
SLIP
SMOCK
SNEAKERS
SOCKS
SOMBRERO
STAYS
STOCKINGS
STOLE
SUIT
SWEATER
SWIMWEAR

## ACROSS

**1** Small red salad ingredient (6,6)

**8** Disgust, abhorrence (5)

**9** Put into the care of (7)

**10** Popular ice-cream flavour (3-3-6)

**12** Close (your fist) tightly (6)

**14** Catlike (6)

**17** Branch of dentistry (12)

**21** Stretchy material (7)

**22** Childminder (5)

**23** Bookishness (12)

## DOWN

**1** Prepare (a meal) (4)

**2** Enjoyer of good food (7)

**3** Ballroom dance (5)

**4** Chic, fashionable (6)

**5** Another name for marsh gas (7)

**6** Sightseeing outings (5)

**7** Dazed (7)

**11** Child's toy vehicle (7)

**13** Variety of cream (7)

**15** Fragrant smoke (7)

**16** Blanket-like cloak (6)

**18** Person's feature or mannerism (5)

**19** Barbecue utensils (5)

**20** Body parts used for seeing (4)

# PUZZLE 66

## Curtains

```
H G M H G U Y G M E F E H U E
O D R A D N I L B R E L L O R
E C U R T A I N H O O K S G V
T M S O R T I N E A E H Y E O
U A U N E D S R I T A O N P I
O M P V W S T E Q L S E E Q C
K A N E A A K A R S T N E S I
C T O I S L R C L I S T R G R
A E M F A T A D A E C E S W B
L R S D N P R N R B T N I H A
B I D U I E B Y C T E N O T F
E A L P O L E S U E D I P V A
L L O N I M R H R O E I T S O
A T F N Y E S C W Y P O N A C
E C D D L T S R R A I L I N G
```

BLACKOUT
CANOPY
CURTAIN HOOKS
DRAWN
FABRIC
FOLDS
LINING
MATERIAL
NETS
OPEN
PELMET
POLES
RAILING
ROLLER BLIND
SCREENS
SHUTTERS
TAPESTRY
TIEBACKS
VALANCE
VENETIAN BLIND
WINDOW

## ACROSS

1 Rodent living under the streets (5,3)
5 Elegant, stylish (4)
9 Very strong winds (5)
10 Saw through (a plot) (7)
11 Brogue, loafer, eg (4)
12 Citizen of a particular country (8)
14 Dublin's river (6)
15 Have in mind (6)
18 Overdo it (2,3,3)
20 Machine for weaving (4)
23 Laundered (7)
24 Monarch's time in office (5)
25 Allows (4)
26 Capital city of Finland (8)

## DOWN

1 Exhales audibly (5)
2 Hotel that gave its name to a salad (7)
3 Go upwards (4)
4 TV mast (6)
6 Greek lady of Troy (5)
7 Hugged (7)
8 Atmospheric (music) (7)
13 Book's brave female lead (7)
14 Systematic (7)
16 Feeling (7)
17 Lumber (with) (6)
19 Handle (5)
21 Welsh strait (5)
22 Greek god of love (4)

## Doll's House

| | | | | | | | | | | | | | | |
|---|---|---|---|---|---|---|---|---|---|---|---|---|---|---|
| S | W | I | N | D | O | W | S | Y | K | H | E | G | H | W |
| T | A | Y | F | G | I | S | E | A | T | I | S | C | E | A |
| N | L | H | A | O | E | N | E | C | T | T | A | I | A | L |
| I | E | L | G | R | O | C | E | D | I | R | C | N | S | L |
| A | K | R | U | T | I | R | A | K | P | E | R | H | N | P |
| P | E | G | Y | C | O | L | L | E | C | T | I | O | N | A |
| E | I | R | C | L | S | R | T | O | A | E | A | I | T | P |
| F | E | H | U | H | N | A | R | R | R | S | T | E | I | E |
| L | T | G | A | T | O | N | M | U | F | A | S | E | C | R |
| M | N | N | R | N | A | U | T | Y | A | L | P | S | I | D |
| O | H | S | E | M | D | I | S | U | S | M | O | O | R | I |
| D | T | G | E | D | N | M | N | E | E | P | A | L | N | R |
| E | E | N | L | R | O | I | A | I | S | O | A | T | Y | E |
| L | T | C | U | U | D | O | L | D | M | R | G | N | M | I |
| S | S | F | A | K | E | H | W | E | E | D | O | O | R | S |

CARPET
COLLECTION
DECOR
DISPLAY
DOORS
FIGURES
FURNITURE
GLUE
HAND-MADE
HOUSE
KITS
MINIATURE
MODELS
ORNAMENTS
PAINTS
ROOF
ROOMS
STAIRCASE
WALLPAPER
WINDOWS
WOODEN

# PUZZLE 69

## ACROSS

**7** In the decimal system (6)
**8** Unwrapped (6)
**9** Chance (4)
**10** Curb (8)
**11** Affected by severe cold (11)
**14** Varying from the average (3-8)
**18** Oily fish, often smoked (8)
**19** Squeaking rodents (4)
**20** Traditional Austrian frock (6)
**21** Speak indistinctly (6)

## DOWN

**1** Wickedness or black magic (7)
**2** Arduous journey (4)
**3** Ancient Egyptian beetle (6)
**4** Close-fitting stiff bodice (6)
**5** Take under your wing (8)
**6** Blue jeans (5)
**12** Decorative gathering on dresses (8)
**13** Brown skin spot (7)
**15** Walk leisurely (6)
**16** Coolness and poise (6)
**17** France's capital (5)
**19** Brief note (4)

## Fabrics

| | | | | | | | | | | | | | | |
|---|---|---|---|---|---|---|---|---|---|---|---|---|---|---|
| G | W | J | K | Z | Q | R | S | R | G | S | M | P | R | S |
| O | B | R | S | U | S | O | A | T | V | Y | U | C | D | E |
| R | G | M | A | A | P | F | E | L | T | E | S | S | O | U |
| T | T | R | M | F | U | L | A | S | O | I | L | C | D | Q |
| R | U | T | A | I | E | A | B | G | L | E | I | V | G | I |
| N | L | M | D | N | S | K | A | K | M | O | N | R | E | P |
| T | L | I | N | E | N | B | I | I | A | E | P | W | N | T |
| Y | E | A | U | D | A | E | N | O | C | I | L | A | C | C |
| D | L | S | C | R | E | E | R | A | O | I | T | E | N | A |
| F | R | Y | D | R | D | E | C | O | T | T | O | N | S | E |
| O | I | I | E | S | E | L | W | T | G | M | F | N | A | B |
| B | N | E | L | S | A | P | C | T | N | O | Y | A | R | A |
| E | D | N | I | R | R | T | E | S | U | L | I | O | T | I |
| E | P | A | O | L | N | E | I | R | O | E | I | S | O | Z |
| A | T | Y | V | E | C | D | J | N | L | R | G | N | M | E |

BAIZE
CALICO
COTTON
CREPE
DAMASK
DENIM
FELT
FLANNEL
GABARDINE
JERSEY
LINEN
MUSLIN
NYLON
PIQUE
RAYON
SATIN
SILK
TULLE
TWEED
VELVET
VOILE

## ACROSS

7 Describe succinctly (11)
8 Wearing a yashmak (6)
9 Preferable (6)
10 Emphasised (8)
11 In the altogether (4)
12 Thames at Oxford (4)
14 Spangly, sparkly (8)
17 Brief portion of time (6)
19 Cancer or Capricorn, for example (6)
20 Florida's capital (11)

## DOWN

1 Discard (6)
2 Instruments used by a surgeon (8)
3 Long-handled digging tools (6)
4 Knighted (6)
5 Tapered tuck in a garment (4)
6 Myth (6)
11 Popular vegetarian dish (3,5)
13 Athletic (6)
14 Black Forest cake? (6)
15 Desk accessory (2-4)
16 Brought up (children) (6)
18 French word for 'she' (4)

# PUZZLE 72

## Fashion Designers

| | | | | | | | | | | | | | | |
|---|---|---|---|---|---|---|---|---|---|---|---|---|---|---|
| W | N | J | M | A | R | Y | Q | U | A | N | T | X | Q | T |
| G | E | S | R | T | Y | R | R | E | B | R | U | B | J | I |
| I | R | A | D | O | S | L | C | T | G | S | I | T | I | T |
| V | U | E | R | D | I | H | A | N | G | L | D | E | M | U |
| E | A | N | P | M | A | D | A | C | L | S | N | T | M | R |
| N | L | F | I | N | A | W | N | E | R | E | E | S | Y | R |
| C | H | I | E | C | A | N | R | A | V | O | F | E | C | E |
| H | P | L | U | R | O | A | I | A | T | O | I | B | H | C |
| Y | L | D | E | S | P | L | L | T | E | S | A | X | O | L |
| G | A | V | S | A | A | E | E | O | T | R | I | E | O | A |
| P | R | W | I | E | N | N | D | F | B | L | S | R | D | G |
| O | T | H | E | T | S | E | N | O | A | O | L | A | H | U |
| T | C | G | I | F | B | E | U | A | D | R | R | S | O | C |
| S | T | N | E | H | E | R | M | E | S | P | H | P | L | C |
| N | O | E | O | N | I | H | C | S | O | M | I | I | S | I |

ANNA SUI
ARMANI
BARBOUR
BURBERRY
CERRUTI
CHANEL
CHRISTAN DIOR
FENDI
GIVENCHY
GUCCI
HERMES
JIMMY CHOO
LACROIX
MARY QUANT
MOSCHINO
NICOLE FARHI
PRADA
RALPH LAUREN
SCHIAPARELLI
VALENTINO
VERA WANG

# PUZZLE 73

**ACROSS**

**7** Equipment for playing music (5,6)
**8** Cheese and egg flan (6)
**9** Just about (6)
**10** Make your home in a new place (8)
**11** Genteel woman (4)
**12** Chopped (of timber) (4)
**14** Adolescent (8)
**17** Carry out (a crime) (6)
**19** Safe house (6)
**20** Sustenance, food (11)

**DOWN**

**1** Convince (6)
**2** Formal midday meal (8)
**3** Commercial (6)
**4** Whirl (6)
**5** List element (4)
**6** Happily occupied (6)
**11** Form of petrol (4-4)
**13** Approximately (6)
**14** Choice delicacy (6)
**15** Like soil (smell or taste) (6)
**16** Age at which you become an octogenarian (6)
**18** Handle roughly (4)

# PUZZLE 74

## Feelings

| | | | | | | | | | | | | | | |
|---|---|---|---|---|---|---|---|---|---|---|---|---|---|---|
| T | S | U | L | R | E | D | N | A | W | M | Y | B | F | J |
| S | Y | M | P | A | T | H | Y | X | S | T | G | C | L | L |
| G | S | C | L | W | B | N | C | A | I | R | L | G | T | F |
| L | A | S | O | O | O | C | I | N | A | J | R | T | A | B |
| L | N | R | E | I | G | S | A | T | Y | O | M | O | Y | R |
| T | R | O | S | N | U | V | I | E | R | Y | I | A | C | W |
| Y | H | N | I | H | L | T | H | N | E | C | L | R | N | A |
| D | E | A | T | S | U | U | O | D | S | V | I | T | E | A |
| T | E | N | P | D | S | A | F | E | I | R | O | E | D | B |
| A | E | S | E | P | N | A | O | R | M | I | L | L | N | O |
| T | N | G | P | X | I | M | P | N | E | F | A | B | O | R |
| E | C | G | I | A | D | N | R | E | H | E | U | I | P | E |
| O | T | E | E | E | I | V | E | S | A | L | H | N | S | D |
| R | T | S | U | R | P | R | I | S | E | E | I | C | E | O |
| Y | A | I | R | O | H | P | U | E | S | O | A | T | D | M |

ANGER
ANXIETY
BOREDOM
CHEERFULNESS
DESPAIR
DESPONDENCY
ENTHUSIASM
EUPHORIA
GRATITUDE
HAPPINESS
JOY
LOVE
MISERY
PASSION
SURPRISE
SYMPATHY
TENDERNESS
TENSION
VANITY
WANDERLUST
WORRY

**ACROSS**

1 Angola's continent (6)
5 Poorly (6)
8 Common breed of black and white cow (8)
9 Weave together (4)
10 Begging request (4)
11 Was affiliated (to a club) (8)
12 Out-of-form occasion (3,3)
13 Coronet, tiara (6)
15 Warehouse worker (8)
18 Young lady (4)
19 Go after prey (4)
20 Appealing to high-income consumers (8)
21 Tight-fitting (jeans) (6)
22 Bend the knees in greeting (6)

**DOWN**

2 Load-carrying vehicle (4-4,5)
3 Dublin's country (7)
4 In a friendly way (7)
5 Cancel (5)
6 Compare (5)
7 Quiet state (13)
13 Energetic, forceful (7)
14 Ardent fan (7)
16 Snitch, tattle (3,2)
17 Dull brown (hair) (5)

# PUZZLE 76

## Footwear

| | | | | | | | | | | | | | | |
|---|---|---|---|---|---|---|---|---|---|---|---|---|---|---|
| H | K | N | H | N | G | D | N | P | B | H | I | N | T | D |
| S | A | N | D | A | L | A | O | L | A | C | E | U | P | S |
| R | G | I | N | A | T | L | L | O | S | M | I | L | P | R |
| I | H | A | N | C | F | D | R | O | T | I | A | B | U | G |
| E | R | E | P | P | I | L | S | T | S | N | M | B | M | K |
| L | R | T | I | C | O | U | R | T | S | H | O | E | P | I |
| L | A | L | E | W | H | A | S | N | U | O | E | E | S | R |
| I | F | C | D | R | I | N | T | S | T | A | I | S | E | L |
| R | T | E | N | N | E | A | I | R | E | E | O | K | I | O |
| D | T | W | E | G | O | M | L | S | F | I | A | A | B | A |
| A | B | R | A | E | T | C | E | D | A | E | L | R | N | F |
| P | S | R | G | D | P | H | T | U | N | C | O | L | I | E |
| S | O | O | T | E | E | A | T | S | N | G | C | R | E | R |
| E | L | E | I | O | E | R | O | A | U | T | E | O | C | W |
| C | D | R | G | N | P | M | S | E | L | U | M | I | M | S |

BOOT
BROGUE
CLOG
COURT SHOE
ESPADRILLE
FLIP-FLOP
GALOSHES
LACE-UPS
LOAFER
MOCCASIN
MULE
PEEP-TOE
PLIMSOLL
PUMPS
SANDAL
SLIPPER
SNEAKER
STILETTOS
TRAINERS
WADERS
WELLIES

# PUZZLE 77

### ACROSS

**1** Cinched around the middle (4-7)
**9** Realistic rather than emotional (13)
**10** Manicure implement (4-4)
**12** Release (a knot) (4)
**14** Seize (power) by force (5)
**15** Genuinely, really (5)
**19** Loads, lots (4)
**20** Burn without a flame (8)
**22** Fear of spiders (13)
**24** All in, tired (5,2,4)

### DOWN

**2** Beast of burden (3)
**3** Apron with a bib (8)
**4** With great interest (6)
**5** Apple pip, eg (4)
**6** Caught up, trapped (9)
**7** Bright (weather) (5)
**8** Be in flower (5)
**11** Hint (9)
**13** Squatted close to the ground (8)
**16** Besmirch (5)
**17** Bring in from another country (6)
**18** Built-up (5)
**21** Cast off (4)
**23** Shout of disapproval (3)

# PUZZLE 78

## Gift Ideas

| | | | | | | | | | | | | | | |
|---|---|---|---|---|---|---|---|---|---|---|---|---|---|---|
| I | J | S | W | E | E | T | S | I | S | K | C | O | S | F |
| I | S | R | E | H | C | U | O | V | I | I | G | R | N | L |
| I | N | B | C | V | T | I | F | T | U | O | W | E | N | O |
| I | N | Y | H | Y | O | G | E | I | N | E | R | P | I | W |
| U | N | R | O | R | T | L | I | C | M | A | B | M | G | E |
| N | R | E | C | T | O | I | G | U | A | A | N | A | Y | R |
| U | R | L | O | A | Y | C | F | M | O | L | L | H | T | S |
| I | T | L | L | E | S | R | H | R | A | C | K | E | N | A |
| R | S | E | A | E | E | O | N | A | O | K | L | C | I | T |
| G | M | W | T | P | S | A | S | H | M | E | E | A | E | T |
| B | E | E | E | E | M | N | O | C | C | P | R | U | H | N |
| S | U | J | S | E | I | L | O | A | A | T | A | E | P | A |
| P | V | O | N | A | L | N | R | K | R | R | E | G | I | L |
| S | R | T | O | A | T | B | Y | E | L | R | F | G | N | P |
| N | M | I | S | B | A | T | H | S | A | L | T | S | A | E |

ALCOHOL
BATH SALTS
BRACELET
CHAMPAGNE
CHOCOLATES
FLOWERS
GLOVES
HAMPER
JEWELLERY
MAKE-UP
NECKLACE
NEW OUTFIT
ORNAMENT
PERFUME
PLANT
ROSES
SCARF
SOCKS
SWEETS
TOYS
VOUCHERS

# PUZZLE 79

## ACROSS

**1** Showing preference for one over another (11)
**9** Belonging to that girl (3)
**10** Slightly fizzy wine (9)
**11** Drain of vitality (8)
**12** Carry on the breeze (4)
**14** Affected imitation of sobbing (6)
**16** Millet-like nutritious grain (6)
**18** Duty system (4)
**19** Peak, apogee (4,4)
**22** Co-ordinator (9)
**23** Wordplay (3)
**24** Kept stored (2,9)

## DOWN

**2** See eye to eye (5)
**3** State of unawareness (8)
**4** Distant (6)
**5** (Had) ripped (4)
**6** Support, keep up (7)
**7** Gardener's handcart (11)
**8** Tightening (a muscle) (11)
**13** Bliss (8)
**15** Eight-sided figure (7)
**17** Sentimental trash (6)
**20** Student (5)
**21** Dead keen on (4)

## Handbag

| | | | | | | | | | | | | | | |
|---|---|---|---|---|---|---|---|---|---|---|---|---|---|---|
| D | L | F | Z | D | D | E | A | Y | E | D | R | M | P | N |
| E | I | M | A | O | T | R | F | I | E | U | A | N | U | E |
| O | P | D | I | P | O | C | K | E | T | S | R | T | R | I |
| A | B | E | G | N | A | H | C | E | S | O | O | L | S | B |
| E | A | N | M | P | T | K | O | R | L | S | T | I | E | A |
| E | L | N | Y | S | A | S | U | E | T | A | D | R | L | M |
| A | M | Z | I | P | H | R | O | I | I | T | B | I | A | S |
| P | S | A | L | C | E | O | T | N | A | Y | N | E | R | E |
| H | S | N | E | O | T | C | U | S | L | I | R | K | L | U |
| C | I | L | O | O | H | T | G | L | N | C | M | E | F | S |
| T | A | B | T | I | E | D | O | G | D | N | R | Y | S | S |
| U | U | E | N | I | H | R | O | N | T | E | E | R | A | I |
| L | L | G | N | R | B | S | A | E | I | S | R | I | O | T |
| C | E | N | O | H | P | H | A | A | T | Y | E | N | C | D |
| C | H | A | R | G | E | R | L | F | R | G | N | G | M | I |

BROLLY
CHARGER
CLASP
CLUTCH
FASHION
HAND CREAM
KEYRING
LABEL
LINING
LIP BALM
LOOSE CHANGE
MINTS
PHONE
POCKETS
PURSE
SHOULDER
STITCHING
STRAP
TISSUES
TOTE
ZIP

## ACROSS

**1** Large flightless bird (7)
**5** Biblical son of Isaac and Rebecca (4)
**10** Bladed pole for moving through water (3)
**11** Concerning voting (9)
**12** Asian country (5)
**13** Pledge (6)
**15** Absorbent paper (6)
**17** Knock hard and often (6)
**18** Egg whisk (6)
**20** Baby carriages (5)
**23** Concerning most of the 19th century (9)
**24** Dedicated poem (3)
**25** Invalid (4)
**26** Pertaining to physical feelings (7)

## DOWN

**2** Fathered (5)
**3** Another assessment (2-10)
**4** Plant often grown with mustard (5)
**6** Rock layer (7)
**7** Visually awful (4)
**8** Club, association (7)
**9** Women's stretchy trousers (7,5)
**14** Small close group (7)
**16** Paint using a template (7)
**19** Lift up, elevate (5)
**21** Bouquet (5)
**22** Baking chamber (4)

# PUZZLE 82

## Horoscope

| | | | | | | | | | | | | | | |
|---|---|---|---|---|---|---|---|---|---|---|---|---|---|---|
| F | V | Q | C | T | H | L | N | M | R | B | T | E | L | N |
| E | O | T | S | A | F | I | S | H | E | S | A | L | H | R |
| E | N | O | T | E | P | B | E | L | C | G | U | R | M | E |
| N | E | P | O | T | L | R | F | E | N | B | L | H | C | R |
| T | N | E | S | O | T | A | I | E | A | L | G | S | N | A |
| N | A | M | C | O | T | A | C | C | C | S | A | E | P | E |
| O | W | U | O | A | H | N | E | S | O | G | N | L | A | B |
| I | O | T | R | E | R | A | M | S | I | R | N | I | A | R |
| L | R | I | P | U | E | O | U | T | I | L | N | T | W | E |
| G | E | M | I | F | S | I | T | O | G | R | I | V | S | T |
| S | A | B | O | E | R | A | N | I | N | I | M | E | G | A |
| A | R | H | S | A | R | C | H | E | R | U | C | I | O | W |
| T | E | P | U | I | V | L | N | R | E | S | I | L | S | O |
| A | T | Q | U | E | L | R | G | N | I | M | I | S | E | A |
| H | A | S | E | O | U | T | R | P | N | E | A | B | I | O |

AQUARIUS
ARCHER
ARIES
BULL
CANCER
CAPRICORN
CRAB
FISHES
GEMINI
LEO
LIBRA
LION
PISCES
RAM
SAGITTARIUS
SCALES
SCORPIO
TAURUS
TWINS
VIRGO
WATER-BEARER

### ACROSS

**1** Fruitlessly, futilely (2,4)
**4** Curtain-track cover (6)
**9** Dairy animal (3)
**10** Casual trouser-and-bib outfit (9)
**11** Historic keepsake (5)
**12** Gymkhana winner's prize ribbon (7)
**14** Raw salad ingredient (6,5)
**17** Multi-sided shape (7)
**18** Song of mourning (5)
**20** Present formally (9)
**22** Lubricant (3)
**23** Fake, artificial (6)
**24** Keyboard user (6)

### DOWN

**1** Proof of age (2,4)
**2** A, e, i, o, or u (5)
**3** Serving with a summons (9)
**5** Age (3)
**6** Musical expert (7)
**7** Sense of style (5)
**8** Of indeterminate gender (11)
**13** In heartfelt fashion (9)
**15** Form of non-impact exercise (7)
**16** Shoe's lace-hole (6)
**17** Balance, composure (5)
**19** Small digital icon (5)
**21** Choose from top table (3)

# PUZZLE 84

## Jeans

| | | | | | | | | | | | | | | |
|---|---|---|---|---|---|---|---|---|---|---|---|---|---|---|
| Y | S | K | U | S | M | F | O | R | O | L | R | U | N | F |
| O | Y | N | D | C | A | L | R | M | N | A | O | R | I | L |
| L | H | U | O | D | S | T | E | K | C | O | P | S | R | A |
| U | T | E | E | T | A | S | N | O | S | C | T | R | E | R |
| S | D | D | S | I | T | A | T | M | L | O | N | M | N | E |
| P | R | K | O | A | R | U | A | I | N | I | G | A | G | S |
| W | A | H | N | Y | E | E | B | E | T | E | S | U | I | E |
| C | I | T | L | R | S | R | W | A | L | C | T | G | S | O |
| D | N | I | C | E | N | A | C | T | A | I | H | R | E | E |
| E | P | O | I | H | S | L | O | G | G | M | F | I | D | L |
| P | I | A | B | H | E | O | E | H | T | L | E | B | N | C |
| P | P | N | E | R | B | S | T | H | U | A | I | O | T | G |
| I | E | D | E | A | W | A | I | S | T | B | A | N | D | L |
| R | F | R | A | Y | E | D | N | R | E | E | I | O | A | T |
| Y | M | I | N | E | D | E | C | L | R | L | G | N | M | I |

BELT
BOOTLEG
BUTTONS
CREASE
DENIM
DESIGNER
DRAINPIPE
FADED
FLARES
FRAYED
LABEL
LEGS
PATCHES
POCKETS
RIPPED
SEAMS
STITCHING
STONEWASHED
STUDS
TIGHT
WAISTBAND

## ACROSS

**8** Avail yourself of (7)
**9** Communicate by computer (5)
**10** Set of principles (5)
**11** Bring into effect (7)
**12** Pedalled device for keeping fit (8,4)
**16** Living world personified (6,6)
**20** Knitting implements (7)
**23** Behind in order (5)
**24** Tunes for the voice (5)
**25** Craved (for) (7)

## DOWN

**1** Noise of a duck (5)
**2** Escape door (4,4)
**3** Quality of being extremely thorough (6)
**4** Greek cheese (4)
**5** Item used with a mortar in the kitchen (6)
**6** Spanish sparkling wine (4)
**7** Slender hooped earring (7)
**13** Small hotel or pub (3)
**14** Bother, nuisance (8)
**15** In the company of (7)
**17** Join the forces (6)
**18** Beverage sachet (3,3)
**19** Italian design house (5)
**21** Sicily's volcano (4)
**22** High-protein bean (4)

## PUZZLE 86

### Jewellery

| | | | | | | | | | | | | | | |
|---|---|---|---|---|---|---|---|---|---|---|---|---|---|---|
| H | W | V | Q | H | S | P | D | S | G | H | T | U | E | I |
| S | O | D | O | E | M | A | C | R | O | E | I | P | C | S |
| O | A | T | A | M | U | L | E | T | L | R | I | C | A | H |
| U | R | E | E | S | O | D | R | K | D | T | I | H | L | L |
| S | A | K | D | A | O | R | N | B | S | T | C | O | K | I |
| E | I | C | I | P | R | A | M | I | A | O | W | K | C | H |
| M | T | O | A | N | U | R | L | U | O | N | E | E | E | D |
| L | E | L | M | S | R | V | I | R | N | A | G | R | N | B |
| O | I | G | A | T | E | E | B | N | N | I | A | L | R | R |
| S | E | O | N | R | I | L | T | T | G | G | T | A | E | M |
| B | A | B | T | N | I | U | Q | E | S | S | C | A | E | D |
| N | E | R | E | H | S | U | I | O | N | E | T | E | L | P |
| V | A | A | N | W | O | R | C | L | L | G | N | R | E | P |
| P | E | N | D | A | N | T | I | E | S | O | I | A | T | E |
| C | D | L | R | S | G | N | T | M | I | S | A | S | H | E |

AMULET
ANKLET
BANGLE
BEADS
BRACELET
BROOCH
CAMEO
CHOKER
CROWN
DIAMANTE
EARRINGS
GEM
GOLD
LOCKET
NECKLACE
PENDANT
PLATINUM
SEQUIN
SIGNET
SILVER
TIARA

## ACROSS

7 Lady's bedroom (7)
9 Damp (5)
10 Metal milk can (5)
11 No tickets left! (4,3)
12 Be in charge of (3)
13 Inhabitant of Casablanca (8)
16 Impressive performance (5,3)
17 Garden vegetable (3)
19 Brand of white rum (7)
21 Be sparing with (5)
22 Unclothed figures, in art (5)
23 Bring up and care for (7)

## DOWN

1 Overshadow, darken (7)
2 Getting chillier, as the nights draw in (8)
3 Any one of a planet's satellites (4)
4 Inferred (8)
5 Air bed (4)
6 Assert (5)
8 (Hotel) booking (11)
13 Lack faith in (8)
14 Cutout design sewn on to fabric (8)
15 Gladder (7)
18 Black extremely hard wood (5)
20 System of secret words or letters (4)
21 Browse the internet (4)

# PUZZLE 88

## Kitchen Items

| | | | | | | | | | | | | | | |
|---|---|---|---|---|---|---|---|---|---|---|---|---|---|---|
| J | Z | X | U | G | N | L | U | N | E | B | O | H | A | H |
| C | M | I | C | R | O | W | A | V | E | L | D | L | T | G |
| M | F | S | R | I | N | A | S | F | I | L | T | O | U | A |
| N | R | N | I | E | G | D | I | R | F | S | L | T | C | D |
| I | E | E | A | N | H | B | L | G | N | C | M | C | E | S |
| R | E | V | O | I | K | S | A | P | P | H | O | T | N | K |
| E | Z | O | U | S | C | T | A | U | D | O | L | E | S | A |
| M | E | J | T | T | O | O | G | W | K | I | T | A | N | R |
| A | R | O | U | A | E | N | A | E | H | R | S | P | E | E |
| E | P | O | S | I | I | A | R | I | L | S | T | O | G | N |
| T | M | T | F | H | C | A | T | B | B | E | I | T | C | I |
| S | E | D | S | N | R | E | H | O | S | U | I | D | P | A |
| R | O | A | T | E | P | V | R | W | W | A | L | A | N | R |
| R | W | M | I | X | E | R | E | L | I | E | N | S | O | D |
| A | T | R | E | D | N | E | L | B | E | S | L | C | D | L |

- BLENDER
- BOWL
- COOKER
- DISHWASHER
- DRAINER
- FREEZER
- FRIDGE
- HOB
- JUICER
- KETTLE
- MICROWAVE
- MIXER
- OVEN
- PANS
- POTS
- SINK
- STEAMER
- TEAPOT
- TEA TOWEL
- TOASTER
- WASHING UP CLOTH

**ACROSS**

**8** Collect, amass (5)
**9** Edited (7)
**10** Coincide partially (7)
**11** Popular fashion magazine, colloquially (5)
**12** Arthur of Camelot's wife (9)
**14** Cooking pot (3)
**15** Bible's first woman (3)
**16** Causing anxiety to (9)
**19** Do up your laces again (5)
**21** One of the members of the Saturdays (7)
**23** Cookery (7)
**24** Portion, part (5)

**DOWN**

**1** Crowd of people (6)
**2** Petroleum jelly (8)
**3** Any worshipped film star (4)
**4** Mottle with spots (6)
**5** Box, crate (3,5)
**6** Bookie's prices (4)
**7** Be connected to the side of (6)
**13** Brandy (3,2,3)
**14** Experienced a tingling sensation (skin) (8)
**15** Add to, improve (6)
**17** Make less hard (6)
**18** Hansel's fairy-tale sister (6)
**20** Small branch (4)
**22** European mountain range (4)

## Lipstick Colours

| | | | | | | | | | | | | | | |
|---|---|---|---|---|---|---|---|---|---|---|---|---|---|---|
| C | Y | V | T | A | O | A | P | A | P | R | I | K | A | T |
| H | R | M | E | R | E | M | M | I | H | S | F | F | E | G |
| E | R | T | U | N | E | E | C | W | R | R | A | L | D | O |
| S | E | T | N | L | E | P | O | O | I | H | A | A | U | N |
| T | H | E | O | E | L | L | S | V | R | C | T | M | N | N |
| N | C | I | A | B | G | E | O | I | E | A | L | E | W | G |
| U | N | S | O | Y | B | L | D | T | H | I | L | A | A | Y |
| T | E | P | S | U | O | H | U | W | N | W | D | E | C | R |
| D | L | O | D | U | S | A | O | D | I | K | I | T | A | R |
| E | R | N | S | A | S | E | O | I | N | N | L | T | N | E |
| R | U | B | Y | M | I | S | T | I | G | I | E | F | G | B |
| K | A | B | L | E | C | D | P | M | I | R | A | G | E | N |
| N | S | U | R | E | S | O | R | T | F | O | S | H | L | A |
| S | S | U | I | O | T | E | P | V | A | L | N | R | I | R |
| T | E | I | D | S | O | A | T | Y | E | C | D | L | C | C |

ANGELIC
CHERRY
CHESTNUT
CORAL
CRANBERRY
DUSK
FLAME
FRIVOLOUS
INDULGENT
LUST
MIRAGE
MULLED WINE
NUDE
PAPRIKA
PINK DAWN
ROSEBUD
ROSY GLOW
RUBY MIST
SHIMMER
SOFT ROSE
WHISPER

## ACROSS

8 Bisection (9)
9 Witch's bad luck spell (3)
10 Vertical (goalpost) (7)
11 Woman's wallet (5)
12 Inferior horse (3)
14 Earning a monthly wage (8)
17 Container for restaurant leftovers (5,3)
19 Add (up) (3)
21 Relaxed (5)
23 Aggressor (7)
26 Be horizontal (3)
27 Up-to-date nature (9)

## DOWN

1 Publishing (7)
2 Declare positively (4)
3 Person of over-precise morals (4)
4 Firmly etch (into the mind) (6)
5 Plant used in making rope (4)
6 Briefest (8)
7 Eject (5)
13 Sleeker (8)
14 Droop, hang down in the middle (3)
15 Bit of old cloth (3)
16 Building levels (7)
18 Indian term for a vegetable also known as 'ladies' fingers' (6)
20 Wobbly dessert (5)
22 Tenth of an American dollar (4)
24 Exceptionally (4)
25 Podium (4)

## Mail Order

| | | | | | | | | | | | | | | |
|---|---|---|---|---|---|---|---|---|---|---|---|---|---|---|
| T | K | C | O | T | S | S | W | V | Z | Q | H | M | L | H |
| A | P | L | M | A | I | L | H | A | D | A | E | L | G | O |
| N | D | I | M | Z | K | O | I | V | A | E | W | H | N | F |
| Y | T | D | E | S | C | R | I | P | T | I | O | N | U | F |
| E | F | N | R | C | E | U | G | O | L | A | T | A | C | E |
| T | U | D | E | E | E | L | S | S | N | R | U | T | E | R |
| N | R | R | A | M | S | R | O | G | O | O | D | S | I | S |
| E | N | E | Q | N | E | S | A | Y | R | I | S | G | P | E |
| M | I | O | O | U | I | C | R | L | S | G | N | N | O | M |
| Y | T | F | N | O | A | E | A | P | A | I | E | I | S | D |
| A | U | N | R | L | V | N | A | L | K | R | H | P | T | S |
| P | R | D | U | I | I | T | T | C | P | I | O | P | A | T |
| E | E | A | L | L | C | N | A | I | N | E | R | A | G | E |
| R | I | E | S | H | O | P | E | A | T | T | R | R | E | Y |
| E | D | C | C | L | O | T | H | E | S | Y | D | W | L | R |

ADDRESS
CATALOGUE
CLOTHES
DELIVERY
DESCRIPTION
DISPATCH
FURNITURE
GOODS
OFFERS
ONLINE
ORDER
PACKING
PAYMENT
POSTAGE
QUANTITY
RECEIPT
REPLACEMENT
RETURNS
SIZE
STOCK
WRAPPING

| 1 | | 2 | ■ | 3 | ■ | 4 | ■ | 5 | ■ | 6 | | 7 |
|---|---|---|---|---|---|---|---|---|---|---|---|---|
| 8 | | | | | | | | | ■ | 9 | | |
| | ■ | | ■ | | ■ | | ■ | | ■ | | ■ | |
| 10 | | | | | | | ■ | 11 | | | | |
| | ■ | ■ | ■ | ■ | ■ | | ■ | ■ | ■ | | ■ | |
| 12 | | 13 | ■ | 14 | | | | 15 | | | | ■ |
| | ■ | | ■ | | ■ | ■ | ■ | | ■ | | ■ | 16 |
| ■ | 17 | | | | | 18 | | | ■ | 19 | | |
| 20 | ■ | | ■ | ■ | ■ | | ■ | ■ | ■ | ■ | ■ | |
| 21 | | | | 22 | ■ | 23 | | 24 | | 25 | | |
| | ■ | | ■ | | ■ | | ■ | | ■ | | ■ | |
| 26 | | | ■ | 27 | | | | | | | | |
| | ■ | | ■ | | ■ | | ■ | | ■ | | ■ | |

## ACROSS

**8** Necessary equipment (9)
**9** Program on an iPhone (3)
**10** Army regiment's chief (7)
**11** Lip-curling expression (5)
**12** Beetroot colour (3)
**14** Water area for quackers (4,4)
**17** Badly judged (moment) (3-5)
**19** Astrological lion (3)
**21** Distinctive spirit of a culture (5)
**23** Hand down (power or duty) (7)
**26** Be in possession of (3)
**27** Event marking a departure (7,2)

## DOWN

**1** Child supervision facilities (3,4)
**2** Birthstone for October (4)
**3** Mum or Dad's mother (4)
**4** Sloping letter in print (6)
**5** Egyptian goddess, wife and sister of Osiris (4)
**6** Having motherly feelings (8)
**7** Metal spikes on a rider's heel (5)
**13** Marine mammals (8)
**14** Another word for the full stop (3)
**15** Small cushion (3)
**16** Tedium (7)
**18** Equidistant between start and finish (6)
**20** Citrus fruit (5)
**22** Expensive fabric (4)
**24** Mask, disguise (4)
**25** Company emblem (4)

## Make-up

| | | | | | | | | | | | | | | |
|---|---|---|---|---|---|---|---|---|---|---|---|---|---|---|
| Z | B | L | U | S | H | E | R | E | S | N | A | E | L | C |
| D | T | Y | D | M | T | F | U | S | D | T | G | M | E | F |
| M | A | E | R | C | E | C | A | F | S | K | T | N | G | O |
| L | Y | U | B | A | S | E | C | O | A | T | D | S | U | U |
| I | N | A | R | I | T | N | R | A | S | I | T | G | O | N |
| C | M | A | K | E | U | P | R | E | M | O | V | E | R | D |
| N | M | K | I | F | T | A | E | A | Z | W | B | C | E | A |
| E | L | C | D | L | N | H | S | Y | O | N | O | H | R | T |
| P | I | I | T | S | V | C | G | D | E | N | O | E | U | I |
| W | P | T | I | A | A | A | A | I | C | L | N | R | P | O |
| O | G | S | T | R | O | H | R | E | L | I | I | O | B | N |
| R | L | P | A | O | S | C | A | N | L | H | W | N | T | E |
| B | O | I | V | E | N | L | P | P | I | D | G | A | E | N |
| R | S | L | Y | E | E | E | I | O | E | S | I | I | S | R |
| O | S | E | A | R | T | L | R | R | T | Y | H | E | H | D |

BASE COAT
BLUSHER
BRONZER
BROW PENCIL
CLEANSER
CONCEALER
EYE LINER
EYE SHADOW
FACE CREAM
FOUNDATION
HIGHLIGHTER
LIP GLOSS
LIP LINER
LIPSTICK
MAKEUP REMOVER
MASCARA
NAIL VARNISH
POWDER
ROUGE
TONER
TOP COAT

## ACROSS

**8** Adores (5)
**9** Existing in name only (7)
**10** Blow-up toy (7)
**11** Long-handled spoon (5)
**12** Run a risk (4,1,6)
**14** Try to anticipate a person's actions (6-5)
**20** Long-barrelled firearm (5)
**22** Hug (7)
**23** Office stationery gadget (7)
**24** Best of the bunch (5)

## DOWN

**1** Geographical sphere (5)
**2** Assess the worth of (8)
**3** On dry land (6)
**4** Of a racial group (6)
**5** ___ McCartney, designer (6)
**6** Snow buggy (4)
**7** Name of Disney's Little Mermaid (5)
**13** Beauty preparation (8)
**15** Overtly (6)
**16** Abandon (6)
**17** In mint condition (6)
**18** Joint connecting the hand and arm (5)
**19** More up-to-date (5)
**21** Skin alive (4)

# PUZZLE 96

## Patterns

| | | | | | | | | | | | | | | |
|---|---|---|---|---|---|---|---|---|---|---|---|---|---|---|
| D | D | U | D | G | D | Z | M | A | R | B | L | E | D | D |
| E | O | E | H | I | U | E | G | S | N | M | S | O | M | E |
| N | N | S | R | O | A | P | O | H | P | P | U | N | O | L |
| I | S | O | D | U | G | L | A | O | A | O | M | I | T | P |
| L | S | N | E | S | G | O | P | T | T | F | T | I | T | P |
| H | T | U | D | N | S | I | C | O | T | T | C | T | L | A |
| R | I | I | N | G | N | H | F | D | B | E | A | M | E | D |
| S | P | O | A | R | Y | P | E | R | Y | I | R | T | D | D |
| A | P | H | B | N | I | L | I | E | Y | U | C | N | S | R |
| A | L | O | I | E | K | N | L | N | A | R | S | O | E | I |
| L | E | G | B | C | D | S | D | E | P | I | R | T | S | D |
| M | D | A | E | L | I | F | A | B | D | E | Z | A | R | C |
| E | L | R | E | A | C | C | H | E | C | K | E | R | E | D |
| D | F | D | P | T | T | A | R | T | A | N | N | R | H | S |
| U | I | Y | K | A | E | R | T | S | O | E | A | L | N | R |

BANDED
BRINDLED
CHECKERED
CRAZED
DAPPLED
FIGURED
FRECKLED
LINED
MARBLED
MOTTLED
PAISLEY
PATCHY
PATTERNED
PIEBALD
PLAID
SPOTTED
STIPPLED
STREAKY
STRIPED
TARTAN
TATTOOED

### ACROSS

**1** Loose trousers (6)
**5** Loose long-sleeved tunic (6)
**8** Affliction of the eyelid (4)
**9** Annoyance (8)
**10** Devilishly cruel (8)
**11** Adult kittens (4)
**12** Italian city of canals (6)
**14** Tired, drowsy (6)
**16** Exchange (one thing) for another (4)
**18** Brand-name artificial textile fibre (8)
**20** Adorned with gems (8)
**21** Chill (4)
**22** Spirited and determined (6)
**23** Arouse affection (6)

### DOWN

**2** Criss-cross pattern (7)
**3** Spotless (5)
**4** In a dewy-eyed way (13)
**5** London district in which Harrods is located (13)
**6** Betrothed woman (7)
**7** Berkshire race meeting (5)
**13** Obtain a favourable opinion (7)
**15** Mythical character who opened a box (7)
**17** At what place? (5)
**19** Added alcoholic spirit to (5)

# PUZZLE 98

## Women

| | | | | | | | | | | | | | | |
|---|---|---|---|---|---|---|---|---|---|---|---|---|---|---|
| W | A | U | Q | S | G | Y | G | O | P | Q | U | E | E | N |
| F | O | O | W | S | S | E | H | C | U | D | S | C | Y | L |
| G | E | I | P | W | S | O | T | M | F | S | O | L | S | H |
| A | F | M | O | O | C | E | O | T | E | U | I | A | S | A |
| E | R | M | A | B | S | T | R | N | N | L | G | E | E | U |
| N | A | R | O | L | H | T | O | T | L | R | M | T | R | N |
| N | U | E | I | E | E | R | E | A | C | A | S | P | T | T |
| H | L | T | R | N | A | S | S | W | D | A | D | S | I | I |
| Y | E | S | C | B | S | L | R | S | A | A | O | Y | A | E |
| I | I | I | D | A | U | G | H | T | E | R | T | E | W | L |
| M | N | S | S | N | A | R | O | I | B | C | D | C | L | E |
| A | R | E | T | S | N | I | P | S | E | T | N | E | D | G |
| I | F | A | B | C | I | D | N | R | L | H | I | I | S | O |
| D | T | P | A | L | N | M | R | I | L | O | R | N | R | S |
| A | H | E | R | O | I | N | E | T | E | B | Y | E | C | P |

ACTRESS
AUNTIE
BARONESS
BELLE
BRIDE
COUNTESS
DAME
DAUGHTER
DUCHESS
FEMALE
FRAULEIN
HEROINE
LADY
LASS
MAID
MISS
MOTHER
NIECE
PRINCESS
QUEEN
SISTER
SPINSTER
SQUAW
STEWARDESS
WAITRESS
WIFE
WOMAN

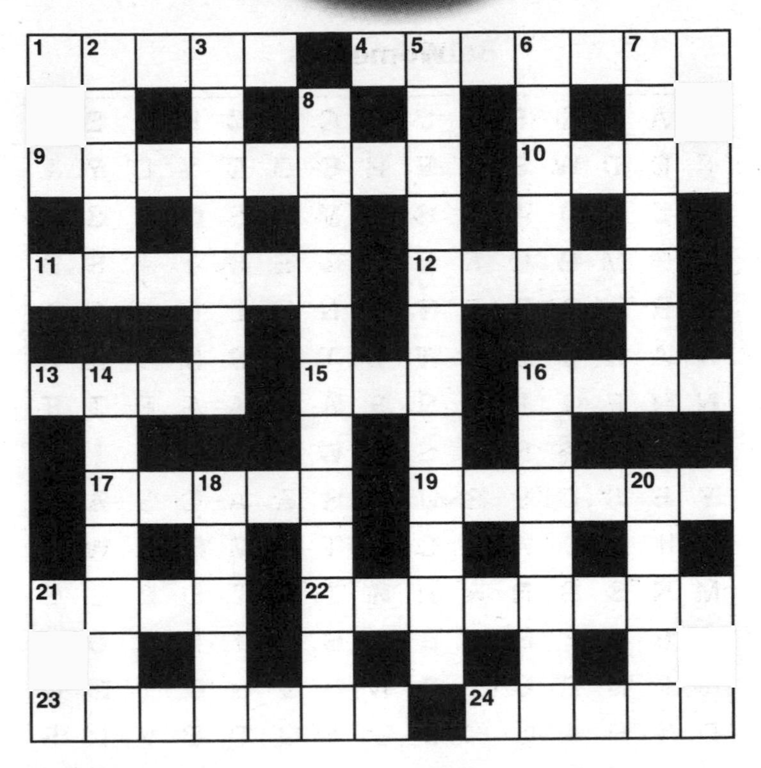

**ACROSS**

- **1** Put on airs, show off (5)
- **4** Rub an itch (7)
- **9** Japanese dish of fish or meat (8)
- **10** Clean with a mop (4)
- **11** Worldwide (6)
- **12** Mentions (5)
- **13** Get wind of (news) (4)
- **15** Bitterly cold (3)
- **16** Auction centre (4)
- **17** Open to view (5)
- **19** Folded (6)
- **21** Highland dress (4)
- **22** Shoe of soft leather (8)
- **23** Lady's decorative umbrella (7)
- **24** Be at ease (5)

**DOWN**

- **2** Potter's machine for shaping round ceramics (5)
- **3** Salon specialising in manicures (4,3)
- **5** External flue (7,5)
- **6** Something worth having (5)
- **7** Rougher (7)
- **8** Be badly affected or hurt by (4,6,2)
- **14** Sexy art or literature (7)
- **16** Knotted threadwork (7)
- **18** Actor in a crowd scene (5)
- **20** Girl's name, or heather (5)

## Baby Animals

| | | | | | | | | | | | | | | |
|---|---|---|---|---|---|---|---|---|---|---|---|---|---|---|
| F | O | A | L | T | E | L | G | A | E | M | F | D | J | Y |
| Q | L | T | S | S | S | N | M | S | D | A | U | C | E | A |
| N | S | A | O | A | R | H | N | S | R | C | O | O | U | A |
| D | R | D | M | M | I | N | E | R | K | H | J | A | S | B |
| O | R | P | G | B | I | N | O | L | F | I | L | L | Y | E |
| W | H | O | U | N | E | W | I | A | N | C | S | T | R | C |
| E | H | L | O | T | I | N | D | R | I | K | A | E | O | E |
| N | M | E | T | S | G | L | O | L | R | T | V | L | I | A |
| E | H | I | L | N | R | U | S | R | E | L | T | G | E | C |
| D | K | I | D | P | E | S | F | O | E | V | R | I | A | O |
| P | Y | B | A | B | F | I | R | T | G | T | E | P | E | N |
| U | N | A | F | R | I | S | Y | E | O | I | T | R | T | M |
| P | A | W | L | E | E | B | A | U | Q | S | C | I | E | D |
| P | N | R | A | H | H | S | U | I | O | T | E | V | L | T |
| Y | A | N | C | F | R | C | Y | G | N | E | T | E | I | S |

BABY
CALF
CHICK
COLT
CUB
CYGNET
DUCKLING
EAGLET
ELVER
FARROW
FAWN
FILLY
FOAL
FRY
GOSLING
HEIFER
JOEY
KID
KITTEN
LAMB
LEVERET
LITTER
PIGLET
PUPPY
SQUAB
TADPOLE
WHELP

# PUZZLE 101

## ACROSS

**1** Plant of the daisy family with brightly coloured flowers (7)
**5** Opposite of 'sad' (5)
**9** Colour of a cat or butterfly (13)
**10** Eager attitude (8)
**11** Acme (4)
**12** Popular herbal remedy (9)
**16** Ledge of a window (4)
**17** Getting to your feet (8)
**19** Union of states (13)
**21** Bread mixture (5)
**22** Chocolate filling (7)

## DOWN

**2** Married secretly (6)
**3** Pertaining to plant life (9)
**4** River that flows through Cologne in Germany (5)
**6** Remains after burning (3)
**7** Simple hoisting device (6)
**8** Professional hostess of Japan (6)
**11** Based on personal accounts (9)
**13** Confidential (information) (6)
**14** Loose Japanese robe (6)
**15** Yet to come into the world (6)
**18** Clothes-drying machine (5)
**20** Multi-seeded fruit (3)

# PUZZLE 102

## Flowers From Bulbs

```
W A E D A F F O D I L A J M X
Q N N S N O I N O P I G U T S
P E I T U H H T J N I S E U R
G M R M E L P Y O O C L S T R
E O E O H E O G A A N S U D R
T N N N B E E I R C I Q G T S
R E T T S B E I D C I P U C I
L L E B E U L B R A W N Y I L
S A I R I S C A H A L C T E L
C I D E S R N O I T L G I H Y
I S L T E R S L R A E X O T R
L E G I M F H B M C I E D R A
L E H A L A S E O A L L I U M
A R T E D Y N E T I N O C A A
P F S N O W D R O P A N R E S
```

ACONITE
ALLIUM
AMARYLLIS
ANEMONE
BEGONIA
BLUEBELL
CROCUS
CYCLAMEN
DAFFODIL
DAHLIA
FREESIA
GLADIOLUS
HYACINTH
IRIS
IXIA
JONQUIL
LILY
MONTBRETIA
MUSCARI
NARCISSUS
NERINE
ONION
SCILLA
SNOWDROP
TULIP

# PUZZLE 103

**ACROSS**

**1** British queen and leader of the Iceni tribe (8)
**6** Tidy, orderly (4)
**8** Animal pests (6)
**9** Twaddle (6)
**10** Corkscrew-shaped locks of hair (8)
**13** Hideous child (4)
**14** Casually arriving (7,2)
**17** Hindu queen (4)
**18** Peak traffic (4,4)
**19** Like an imp (6)
**21** Bird also called a fish hawk (6)
**23** Artificially coloured (4)
**24** Coming into view (8)

**DOWN**

**2** Adult sleepsuit (6)
**3** Mother of a horse (3)
**4** Cosmetic used to hide spots (9)
**5** Assist (3)
**6** Manicurist's bristled item (4,5)
**7** Generation difference (3,3)
**11** Overrated (9)
**12** Rock composed of tiny grains (9)
**15** Low area between hills (6)
**16** Large soup dish (6)
**20** Weeding implement (3)
**22** Small dog (3)

## PUZZLE 104

### Pink Flowers

| | | | | | | | | | | | | | | |
|---|---|---|---|---|---|---|---|---|---|---|---|---|---|---|
| V | A | F | R | E | E | S | I | A | Z | D | D | S | R | T |
| B | I | R | T | U | L | I | P | T | C | C | U | D | R | A |
| G | L | D | P | E | O | T | R | F | L | C | E | H | M | N |
| D | L | E | A | O | C | D | R | E | S | T | B | E | U | E |
| I | E | E | N | H | G | N | M | I | S | O | R | A | S | M |
| A | M | S | S | T | L | A | B | P | E | H | I | N | S | O |
| N | A | O | Y | Y | T | I | E | E | E | N | C | D | Y | N |
| T | C | R | S | I | H | R | A | V | O | T | O | T | L | E |
| H | E | N | S | R | A | S | E | G | O | O | U | A | A | I |
| U | R | E | T | S | A | L | E | P | T | L | Z | N | N | G |
| S | F | B | E | C | D | B | U | N | H | A | G | I | I | P |
| G | E | R | A | N | I | U | M | M | L | L | P | X | O | A |
| R | H | S | I | O | T | E | V | E | I | U | O | P | O | L |
| N | R | E | I | S | O | T | A | Y | L | R | P | X | E | F |
| C | N | O | I | T | A | N | R | A | C | Y | P | D | L | R |

ALYSSUM
ANEMONE
ASTER
AZALEA
BEGONIA
CAMELLIA
CARNATION
CLEMATIS
DAHLIA
DIANTHUS
FOXGLOVE
FREESIA
GERANIUM
HIBISCUS
LUPIN
PANSY
PETUNIA
PHLOX
POPPY
PRIMULA
ROSE
TULIP

## ACROSS

**1** The object over here (4)
**4** Cosmetic pencil used on the mouth (3,5)
**8** Woolly, downy (6)
**9** Highly seasoned stew (6)
**10** Exotic green fruit (4)
**11** As new (8)
**13** Tactfully fall out? (5,2,6)
**16** Group of murderous vigilantes (5,3)
**19** Downfall, collapse (4)
**20** Giant panda's food (6)
**22** Staggered (6)
**23** Precise, particular (8)
**24** Soothe (4)

## DOWN

**2** In a hesitant way (9)
**3** Be adequate (7)
**4** Stockpile (3,2)
**5** Enjoyed yourself at a do (7)
**6** Bullion bar (5)
**7** ___ de cologne, perfume (3)
**12** Excessive desire for affection and attention (9)
**14** Recreation period (4,3)
**15** Pardoned, excused (7)
**17** Having three dimensions (5)
**18** French for 'white' (5)
**21** Domestic fuse unit (3)

# PUZZLE 106

## Problem Page

| | | | | | | | | | | | | | | |
|---|---|---|---|---|---|---|---|---|---|---|---|---|---|---|
| H | B | Q | Z | P | X | A | Q | H | S | B | H | M | G | T |
| S | R | U | S | H | A | Y | D | E | U | C | O | A | R | T |
| N | B | A | G | E | L | R | C | V | O | O | G | G | S | A |
| O | R | N | T | I | C | I | T | N | I | U | P | A | M | M |
| I | H | D | M | Y | O | N | F | N | I | C | R | Z | E | M |
| T | S | A | U | H | D | I | E | D | E | O | E | I | L | E |
| A | F | R | C | R | D | C | A | I | L | R | L | N | B | L |
| L | A | Y | E | A | O | N | R | L | R | O | S | E | O | I |
| E | T | A | N | T | C | S | E | I | V | E | R | S | R | D |
| R | E | T | O | E | T | S | E | E | T | T | P | G | P | F |
| A | B | E | D | R | N | E | H | I | U | I | O | X | T | E |
| C | O | N | S | U | L | T | L | P | L | V | C | A | E | L |
| N | R | N | O | I | S | I | C | E | D | P | E | I | I | P |
| S | O | C | F | A | L | S | E | N | A | M | E | S | S | A |
| T | N | U | A | Y | N | O | G | A | T | Y | E | R | D | M |

ADVICE
AGONY AUNT
CHOICES
CONFIDANT
CONSULT
COUNSELLOR
CRITICISM
DECISION
DILEMMA
EXPERIENCES
FALSE NAMES
FAMILY
GUIDANCE
LETTERS
LOVE
MAGAZINES
PARTNERS
PROBLEMS
QUANDARY
RELATIONS
REPLIES

**ACROSS**

1 Block of frozen water (3,4)
5 Goading instrument (4)
10 Costume used in water sports (7)
11 Doctrine (5)
12 Low bathroom fitment (5)
13 Life-prolonging liquor (6)
15 Early stage of reproduction (6)
17 Ship's mooring device (6)
19 Fluffy shapes in the sky (6)
20 Set (into), fix firmly (5)
23 Courtroom plea of elsewhere (5)
24 Unauthorised by law (7)
25 Breath of relief (4)
26 Banking (on) (7)

**DOWN**

2 Legally named (5)
3 Rural melodies (7,5)
4 Pancake mixture (6)
6 Cantankerous (7)
7 Travel on horseback (4)
8 Cleaned (a wound) (7)
9 Repetition of an event (6,6)
14 Vegetable piece eaten with a dip (7)
16 Hitting hard (7)
18 Be ambitious (6)
21 Food from a pig (5)
22 Conflicts (4)

# PUZZLE 108

## Shades of Pink

| | | | | | | | | | | | | | | |
|---|---|---|---|---|---|---|---|---|---|---|---|---|---|---|
| D | W | E | C | U | P | E | N | G | A | P | M | A | H | C |
| G | E | R | A | N | I | U | M | S | D | T | R | O | S | E |
| T | D | M | T | E | B | I | A | T | T | D | N | I | N | T |
| F | I | N | A | A | S | L | S | O | E | O | O | B | D | C |
| F | T | I | B | G | M | I | E | H | L | N | L | A | S | A |
| U | K | Y | Y | O | E | O | R | E | T | A | I | K | P | N |
| C | M | S | N | R | E | N | M | E | R | W | F | E | M | D |
| H | U | N | H | Y | R | R | T | O | C | L | E | R | I | Y |
| S | G | D | L | O | E | E | C | A | A | S | O | M | R | I |
| I | E | T | E | T | C | N | B | M | A | H | R | I | H | S |
| A | L | G | A | E | O | K | I | P | C | I | L | L | S | T |
| F | B | W | U | A | E | N | I | A | S | D | N | L | R | S |
| I | B | O | T | O | G | E | E | N | P | A | A | E | L | N |
| R | U | E | I | O | R | P | S | O | G | A | R | R | T | Y |
| E | B | C | R | E | T | S | B | O | L | B | L | U | S | H |

BABY
BAKER-MILLER
BLUSH
BUBBLEGUM
CANDY
CERISE
CHAMPAGNE
CORAL
FLAMINGO
FUCHSIA
GERANIUM
HOT
LOBSTER
MAGENTA
PEACH
PUCE
RASPBERRY
ROSE
ROUGE
SALMON
SHOCKING
SHRIMP
WATERMELON

# Solutions

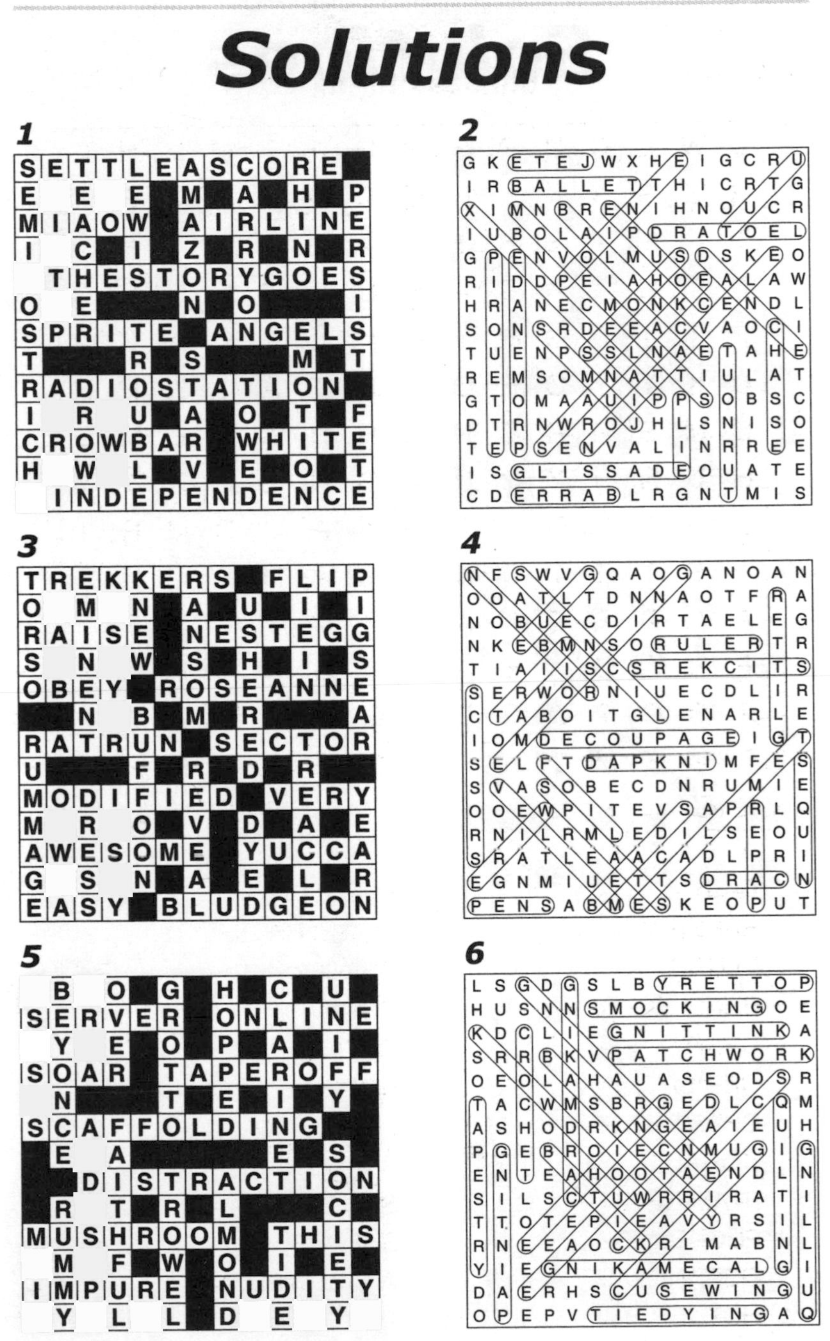

# Solutions

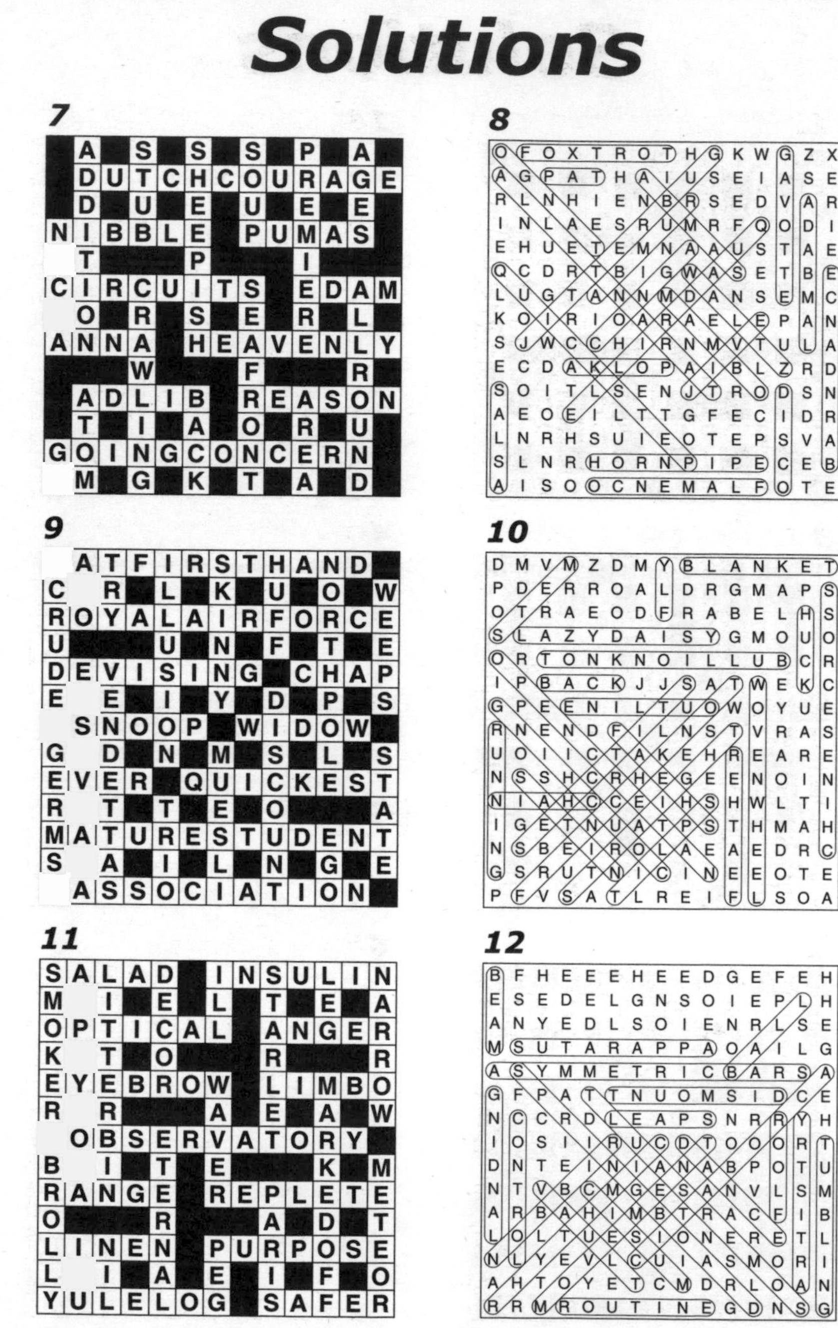

# Solutions

13

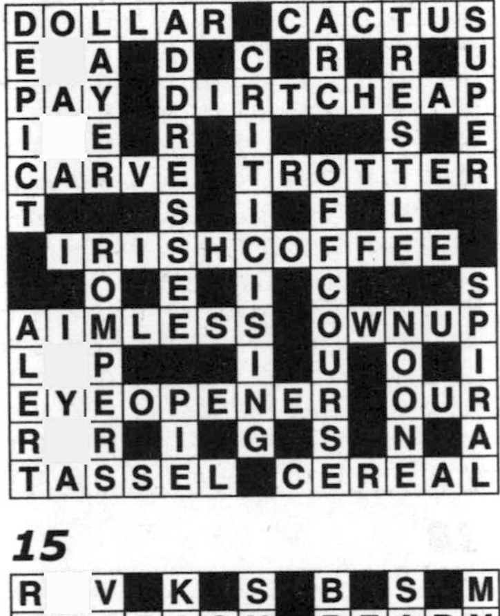

14

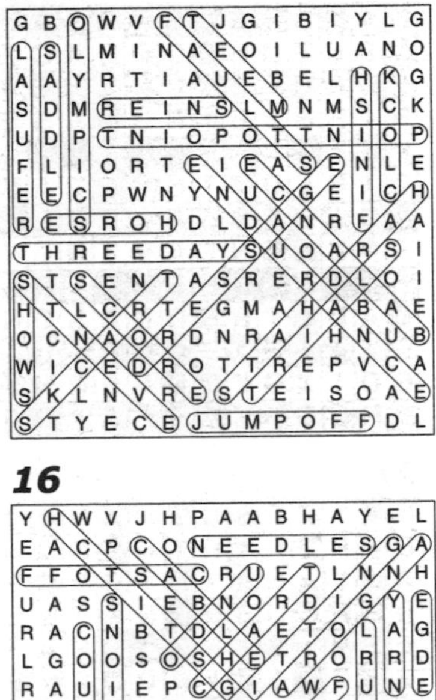

15

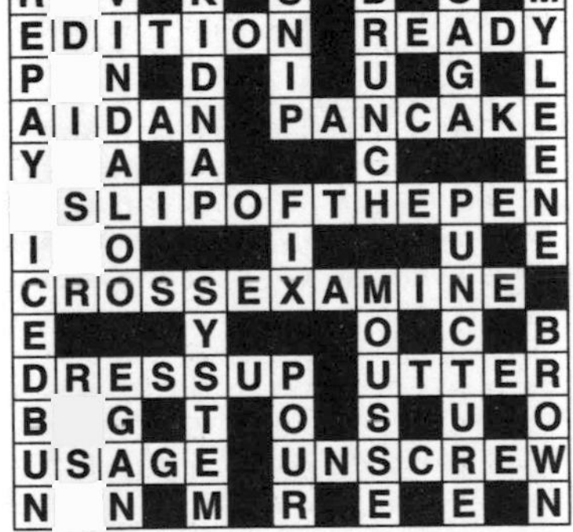

16

17

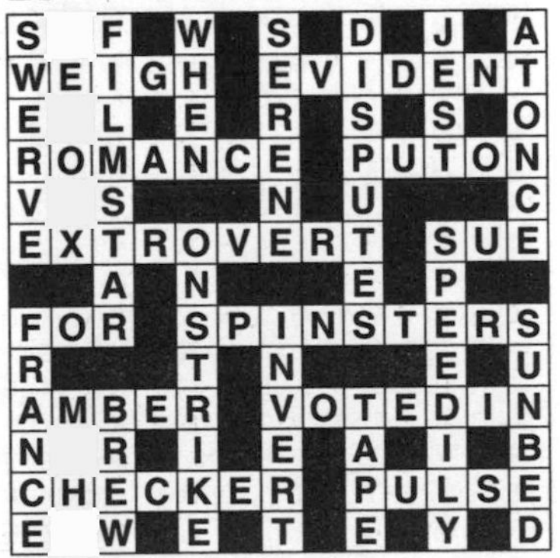

18

| | | | | | | | | | | | | | | |
|---|---|---|---|---|---|---|---|---|---|---|---|---|---|---|
| G | J | U | C | O | A | S | T | E | R | S | T | E | P | S |
| S | T | O | O | B | Y | O | B | W | O | C | W | G | N | R |
| N | T | R | U | D | I | R | G | V | M | P | I | O | R | C |
| O | W | W | U | T | N | N | A | D | E | R | S | I | H | A |
| L | E | O | I | G | E | R | A | T | N | T | T | E | M | R |
| D | I | L | D | N | I | E | S | L | E | A | C | W | S | H |
| F | A | N | K | E | K | R | F | T | I | K | Y | E | T | K |
| A | U | P | T | C | O | L | S | Y | E | N | D | A | R | L |
| S | R | Y | P | L | U | H | E | D | C | A | E | V | I | A |
| H | I | N | I | L | A | B | S | S | R | N | I | E | K | W |
| I | G | A | M | F | E | H | T | A | T | B | A | S | S | L |
| O | S | D | N | R | I | J | H | L | U | E | E | F | G | E |
| N | A | M | E | R | I | C | A | N | E | V | P | I | N | M |
| E | E | O | T | L | E | E | H | C | O | B | O | A | O | A |
| D | L | S | S | P | U | R | S | M | K | N | R | I | L | C |

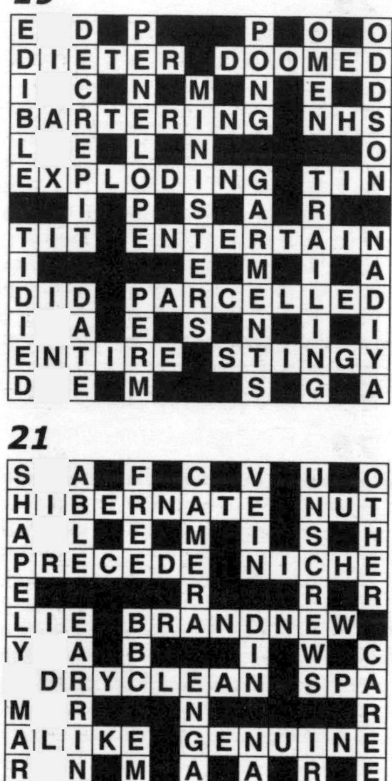

## 22

A U H B A L A N C E A H T A H
F M W A Y G N I H T A E R B U
E S R O R E A D S E O P U E A
F S G A O M M S E D O E P R S
L I H O K L O F H S E L T S U
E N Y C A N S N T T T N I E Y
X O T C T D O U Y C A D R B P
I E I L D E R I A M D N G C A
B N L S K E R P T H O R G H R
I E I P W N M T A A U E C A E
L L G S R I O S S E T N R K H
I S A E W O A I L G F I M R T
T B E O C N D N R S U I D A O
Y E L P A C I R T N A T L E T
N R E I R E L A X A T I O N M

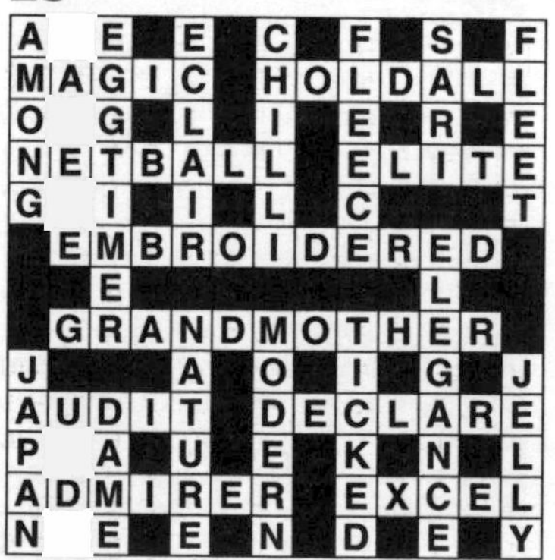

## 24

H S B Y G K S H A D B H W T U
V A L L Y P B R O M A A E E H
U A O I A A E O E C L D I S A
B S R I C E W G R L N M K T I
S A N N E N W H P D L N Y E T
R T U E I C E A D A E O O R A
O I P T E S P T N A R R R P O
T E A E M E H C S R U O L O C
A S T O R I G M A B E C G T R
R D T D E S I G N E R N N S E
O R E I S T I P P L I N G V D
C H R U L T I O K V T E A I N
E L N N T E R E O L I O A N U
D T S A Y E S C C D I L R Y G
N M M N O I S L U M E S I L S

# Solutions

## 26

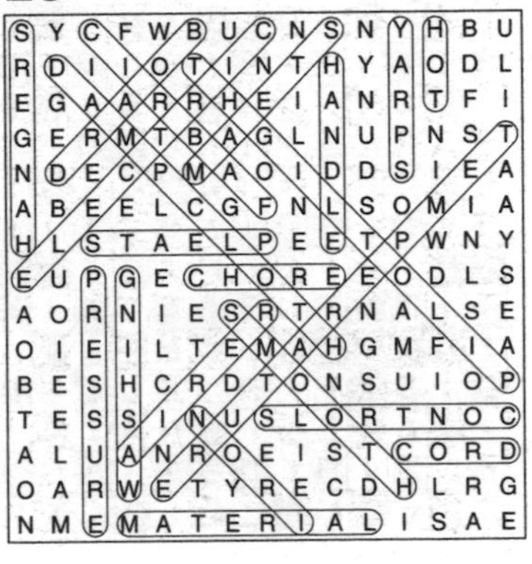

## 28

| | | | | | | | | | | | | | | |
|---|---|---|---|---|---|---|---|---|---|---|---|---|---|---|
| G | K | X | I | I | I | U | I | G | D | T | I | N | U | I |
| S | R | B | A | T | H | S | N | O | C | D | A | R | G | M |
| C | I | E | T | S | E | R | D | A | E | H | N | M | O | R |
| E | F | I | L | L | E | H | S | P | L | A | S | H | S | T |
| N | H | U | I | A | N | W | A | E | O | C | D | E | A | R |
| T | L | T | R | T | X | I | E | F | G | N | L | P | M | K |
| S | E | B | U | B | B | L | E | S | O | D | S | F | O | R |
| T | W | I | B | M | A | E | T | S | N | O | L | A | E | S |
| P | O | H | B | N | U | E | C | A | D | A | L | R | A | O |
| O | T | I | E | S | T | E | C | N | N | N | A | R | R | A |
| S | E | O | R | I | P | L | T | N | A | G | M | W | O | P |
| F | A | E | D | C | D | O | E | N | R | E | A | H | R | S |
| U | I | O | U | T | E | L | N | P | A | T | L | L | R | N |
| R | E | I | C | S | O | A | T | G | E | E | C | C | I | D |
| L | R | G | K | N | E | B | O | R | E | M | I | S | M | A |

## 30

| | | | | | | | | | | | | | | |
|---|---|---|---|---|---|---|---|---|---|---|---|---|---|---|
| Y | T | W | V | Q | O | O | H | O | D | O | P | L | H | O |
| Y | D | A | L | B | E | M | P | I | R | E | L | I | N | E |
| R | D | M | O | O | U | R | F | L | H | O | E | D | R | W |
| E | C | A | A | C | L | T | N | A | L | G | A | R | A | N |
| M | S | I | R | M | I | S | T | K | O | R | T | I | A | W |
| B | E | H | R | T | N | T | Y | O | U | C | S | D | L | S |
| R | V | R | P | B | S | A | T | O | N | T | I | G | N | S |
| O | E | A | R | A | A | S | E | E | T | S | N | O | T | N |
| I | E | I | L | G | T | F | E | U | P | I | M | A | F | I |
| D | L | A | B | A | E | T | C | G | T | C | C | H | R | U |
| E | S | D | K | N | R | S | E | T | N | K | H | E | E | Q |
| R | S | E | U | I | A | O | U | R | I | A | E | M | T | E |
| Y | U | P | V | I | A | C | L | N | N | N | H | S | L | S |
| P | R | E | B | I | S | O | G | A | Y | E | E | C | A | C |
| D | F | I | T | T | I | N | G | S | E | L | D | E | E | N |

# Solutions

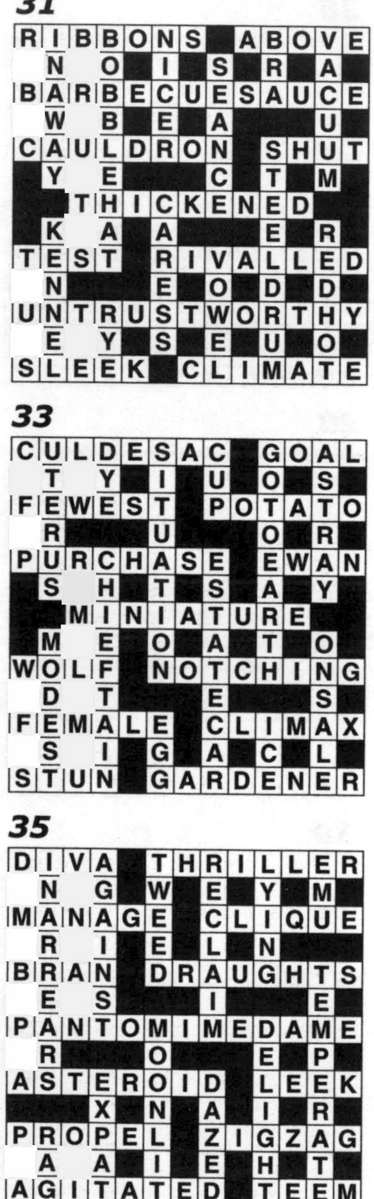


## 32

G C B W V J S T U O Y A D I N
I O N I G E N P D I M O N E Y
N F T B L R I N R A T D G M J
I F N A A O E T F E I A N E S
E E S O D E R H T I S A W E S
S E I R O S S E C C A E H B E
E G S N C A M K O U L T N R O
T I P A A H E W N L O Y U T H
E D O L R C R A E L O V C I S
L T H E P R N R C A M R A E O
E U S I A U Y L T A S G S M F
A R N B R P E D K N R G H M U
I O O C K C R E D I T C A R D
T E P T H V U A L N R L E B I
S O A T S P Y E D L L L L I T

## 34

H S U R B P V N Q P A S T A N
O A T C O L D W A T E R U E Y
E E A P O S I T I E E A H D N
E O T S I E A Q E L L C N O S
T I A C E V P H U N T C Y U E
S D D R A O B G N I N I A R D
P L R U A L K O K I D T E I N
A A R B E G G N O I L T S L Y
T A E B R R R S I C D H E N R
L R H I S E E U O S W W I C E
O L N N T B A E P A O V A L K
L S I G N B S R S T K E I O C
E S O W A U E H A T Y I E T O
C D L R S R E E G N I S N H R
A B O W L R T D R Y I N G G C

## 36

B F U L L C I R C L E Y W J Z
U D D A A S G N I S S O R C B
U A Y N D N A P U A T G E B N
T F I G E H T A O H D N M I L
R T A B L S C N G O R I O G E
T T S A P C R I W N Y V H G A
U H E L I D S E L R A O G I P
S O E D E T O T M V E L N R O
R T E P S W S N A M N A I L F
E N H R R T E N I N U X O Z F
T X I E E O I J R M E S G O A
S F O R R S M E C H O E S Y I
I L C T H I M I R A C L E A T
S E A E B E N D S C I G A M H
S R D U O T E G P E V A L P N

# Solutions

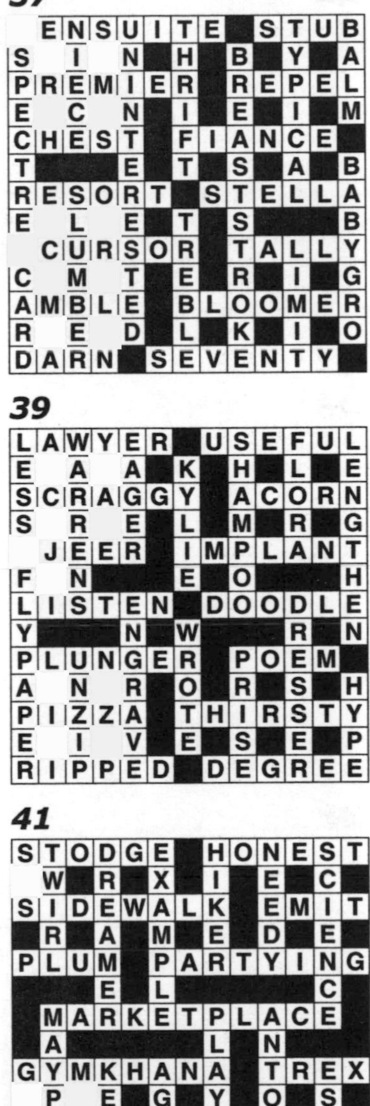

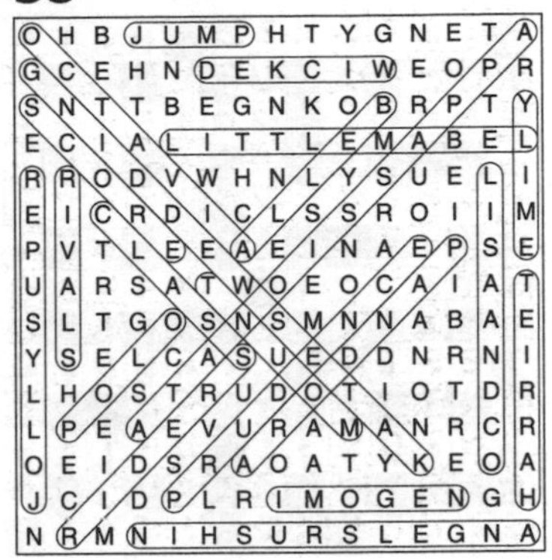

## 40

F R O S A L I N D K J C U A T
T U T P S A O T F H L U C I S
O A L O I V R T B E E S M L S
K I O R T E A D O P I H O I B
K L A N D I U P N C E P D M E
A E S N V E A R N A H O A E A
T D H I A T S A B E S S T P T
H R L E R I R D L I S S O E R
A O N A L F C I E I A R A R I
R C S E O E A U R M T N T C C
I M F B E D N E L I O N C R E
N H S U O T N A A E P N V A N
E I S A B E L L A R E S A O T
E C D L R N M E N O I M R E H
S K A D N A R I M J U L I E T

## 42

Y F E L T R U T K C O M G S P
N C H E S H I R E C A T S T F
T B N S Y L G A I A N P W R L
W O S S O F I L Q L T H N U A
S O P D O I S L U B I M E O M
R L N A R S G I E T N S E C I
O E R D E A I P E E P W E N N
Y E T H E T C R N L S R D C G
R A C T O R A E I E A N R A O
R U S E A B L T O H I O I G L
D G F A B H A A H B Q E N N R
H A N I D L D C N U S I K U I
O K T T I E R A E D K P M A L
N R E C E A I T M S O A E T Y
E D E Y M L R D O R M O U S E

# Solutions

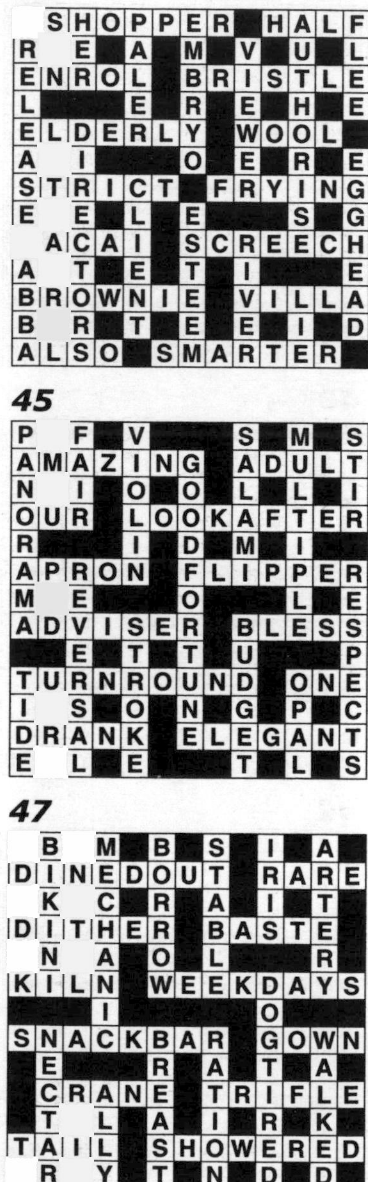

## 44

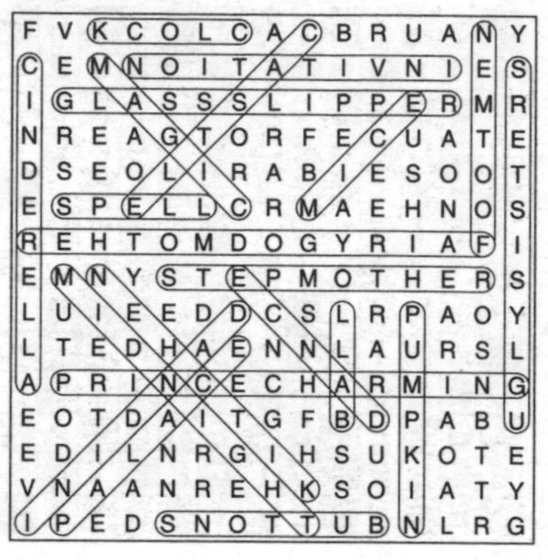

## 46

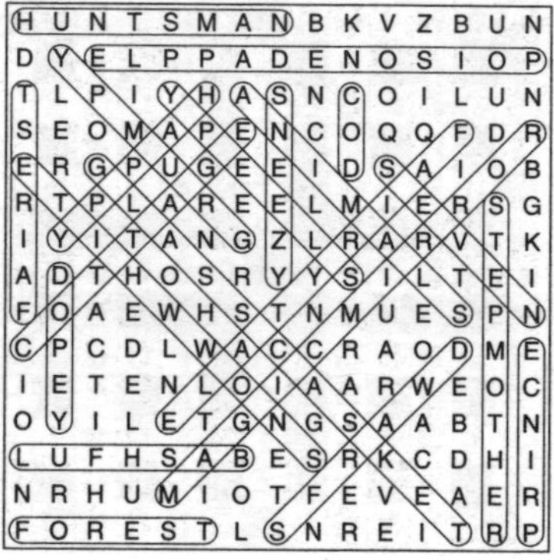

## 48

| | | | | | | | | | | | | | | |
|---|---|---|---|---|---|---|---|---|---|---|---|---|---|---|
| G | P | V | R | N | R | T | A | R | I | K | A | H | S | G |
| H | P | C | R | R | E | S | I | O | T | C | R | K | G | M |
| S | K | E | L | I | S | L | P | F | B | S | E | N | A | O |
| U | A | T | R | J | F | H | L | J | F | C | U | I | N | K |
| B | S | L | O | O | C | R | O | A | N | A | C | P | A | B |
| E | T | E | I | S | G | R | N | O | Y | A | N | T | M | I |
| T | S | O | R | S | K | T | Y | E | T | L | I | Y | P | L |
| A | H | N | U | S | O | E | E | S | C | E | I | S | R | L |
| K | O | I | E | T | B | N | A | T | M | L | U | L | U | I |
| E | N | N | R | O | H | N | M | E | R | E | H | C | E | E |
| S | Y | E | O | N | A | A | L | O | Z | I | T | G | N | M |
| A | F | E | C | E | N | U | Y | R | Y | Z | H | S | I | U |
| A | I | L | E | M | A | J | I | O | O | E | A | T | V | E |
| P | V | N | R | E | I | S | O | A | T | T | T | Y | A | E |
| C | R | G | A | B | R | I | E | L | L | E | G | N | J | M |

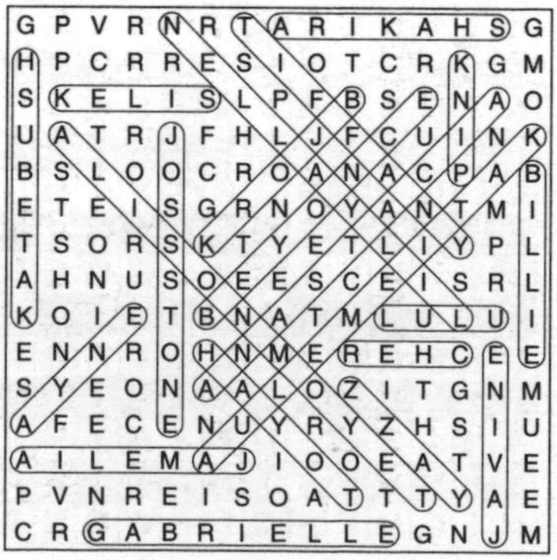

# Solutions

49

50

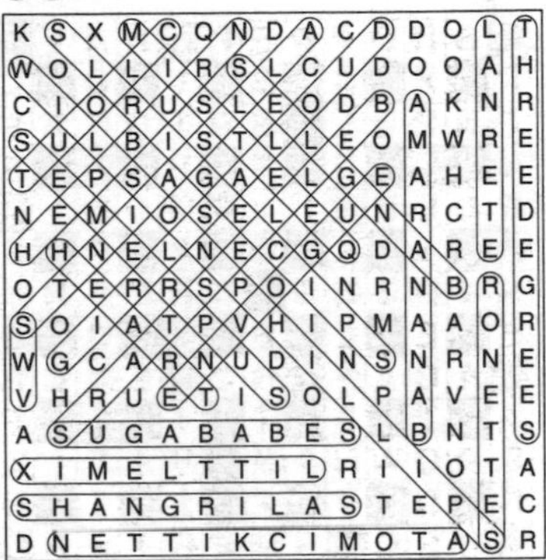

51

52

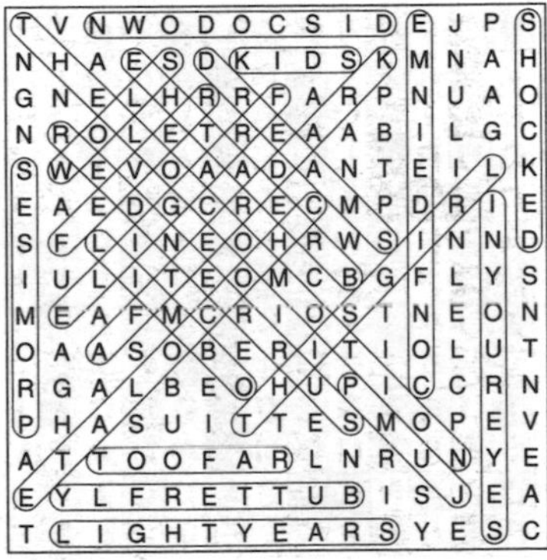

53

54

C F J Z L L N N P N T W N T C
H N P O Y I L T F N H S P H E
E O C R D T K E C I S U M O M
R R R N S O E E T T U I A L E
I O A P T U W E A O P S H I U
S E N T G A H U Y V T C D D C
H N E O S E K S S A I E A A S
O I V I A Y S E Y T N R V Y E
A L E T S E K O A A I L G I R
T R R G R M F C M B A B C I L
D E Y D N H S A U U O I O T N
E D B F R O Z E N L P W A L N
R R O L R I G L A I R E T A M
E O D I N R E L B M A G S O A
T B Y G E D E A R J E S S I E

# Solutions

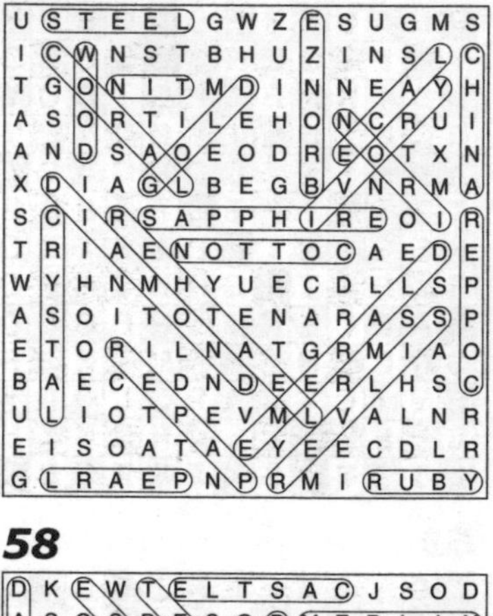

## 58

| D | K | E | W | T | E | L | T | S | A | C | J | S | O | D |
|---|---|---|---|---|---|---|---|---|---|---|---|---|---|---|
| A | S | O | S | B | E | S | O | B | M | E | R | L | I | N |
| H | T | Y | D | R | D | R | E | M | S | O | T | F | T | G |
| A | L | E | S | L | O | D | R | E | O | D | T | I | R | U |
| L | B | I | E | E | I | H | T | U | M | S | K | O | U | I |
| A | T | I | A | V | J | O | U | S | T | I | N | G | O | N |
| G | H | I | E | M | L | F | E | W | N | Y | A | U | C | E |
| S | E | R | D | E | N | S | A | R | F | W | O | I | T | V |
| T | E | E | M | A | N | I | R | L | A | L | S | E | H | E |
| B | O | A | I | T | R | G | A | I | C | M | A | F | G | R |
| A | C | B | E | C | D | T | N | H | N | O | R | G | I | E |
| N | Y | R | L | A | V | I | H | C | C | H | N | S | N | U |
| N | I | O | T | E | A | L | N | U | R | E | I | R | K | S |
| E | O | A | T | Y | E | H | C | D | R | L | R | G | Y | N |
| R | M | L | A | N | C | E | S | I | N | O | L | A | V | A |

## 60

| C | R | E | P | M | A | H | G | M | F | W | V | D | N | N |
|---|---|---|---|---|---|---|---|---|---|---|---|---|---|---|
| A | M | O | D | I | N | A | N | O | T | E | C | A | S | E |
| R | P | O | I | N | B | O | E | D | L | M | I | N | E | O |
| R | I | T | R | D | K | T | X | O | B | H | C | N | U | L |
| I | R | F | N | E | R | I | I | E | L | N | S | E | S | O |
| E | G | A | D | U | S | S | T | K | R | T | I | U | G | E |
| R | H | L | N | N | A | A | C | B | M | S | I | H | A | O |
| R | R | K | T | T | I | A | C | E | A | T | W | A | B | H |
| E | N | U | C | T | P | E | D | F | C | G | G | T | T | O |
| S | L | H | C | K | E | S | Z | A | E | A | Z | B | E | L |
| I | E | R | C | K | O | K | S | I | W | I | T | O | P | D |
| L | E | A | N | R | S | E | S | S | S | E | R | X | R | A |
| A | B | O | I | L | T | A | M | A | F | E | D | B | A | L |
| V | N | R | S | U | I | O | C | T | B | E | P | V | C | L |
| L | L | U | G | G | A | G | E | K | N | P | O | U | C | H |

# Solutions

## 61

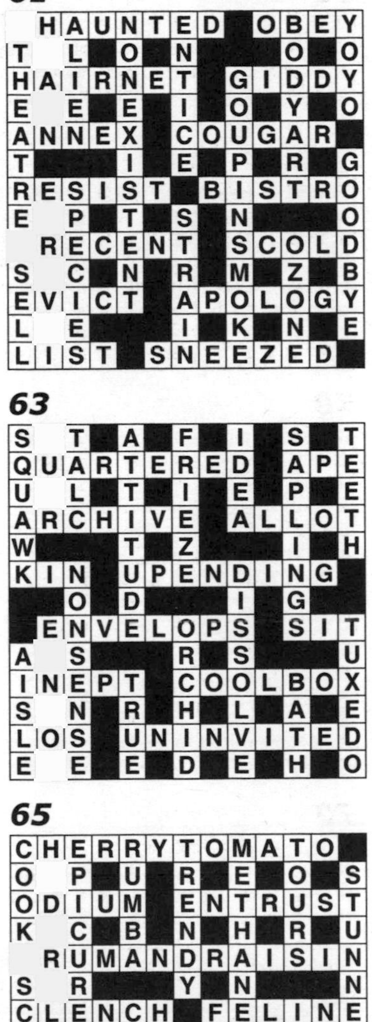

## 62

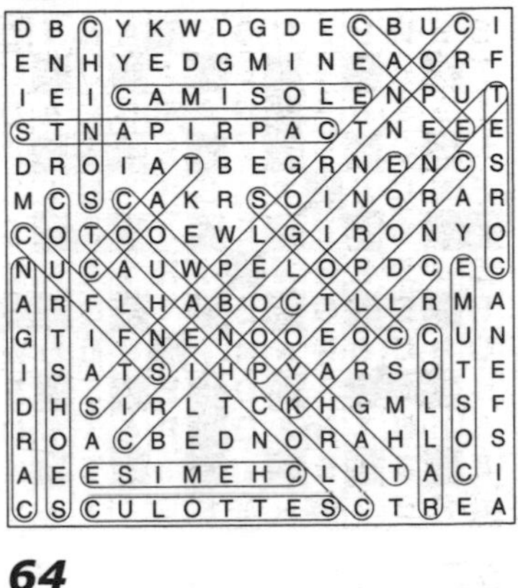

## 63

## 64

```
E D S U P S O C K S Y K F S D
L E U R T E N P E D C N T L S
O E B R E H S U I O E O N I Y
T T O Y E K D C M L C G M N A
S H I N E P A S A K O T F G T
S S T I U S I E I R E L H B S
O U K N E O D N N R F T I A A
R B E C S L G G N S M O R C T
E I A E A S P S T R I K S K H
R N Y U R L E A A C H H D S L
B R A O O I S R T N A S E N A
M R E S N O I I L W D T A G M
O F L A G B E C L D N A R S H
S I U I S W I M W E A R L O T
P R E T A E W S E P A L N S R
```

## 65

## 66

```
H G M H G U Y G M E F E H U E
O D R A D N I L B R E L L O R
E C U R T A I N H O O K S G V
T M S O R T I N E A E H Y E O
U A U N E D S R I T A O N P I
O M P V W S T E Q L S E E Q C
K A N E A A K A R S T N E S I
C T O I S L R C L I S T R G R
A E M F A T A D A E C E S W B
L R S D N P R N R B T N I H A
B I D U I E B Y C T E N O T F
E A L P O L E S U E D I P V A
L L O N I M R H R O E I T S O
A T F N Y E S C W Y P O N A C
E C D D L T S R R A I L I N G
```

# Solutions

## 68

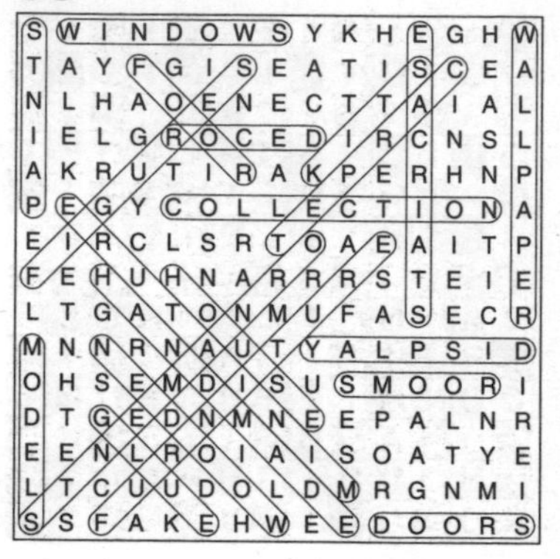

## 70

| | | | | | | | | | | | | | | |
|---|---|---|---|---|---|---|---|---|---|---|---|---|---|---|
| G | W | J | K | Z | Q | R | S | R | G | S | M | P | R | S |
| O | B | R | S | U | S | O | A | T | V | Y | U | C | D | E |
| R | G | M | A | A | P | F | E | L | T | E | S | S | O | U |
| T | T | R | M | F | U | L | A | S | O | I | L | C | D | Q |
| R | U | T | A | I | E | A | B | G | L | E | I | V | G | I |
| N | L | M | D | N | S | K | A | K | M | O | N | R | E | P |
| T | L | I | N | E | N | B | I | I | A | E | P | W | N | T |
| Y | E | A | U | D | A | E | N | O | C | I | L | A | C | C |
| D | L | S | C | R | E | E | R | A | O | I | T | E | N | A |
| F | R | Y | D | R | D | E | C | O | T | T | O | N | S | E |
| O | I | I | E | S | E | L | W | T | G | M | F | N | A | B |
| B | N | E | L | S | A | P | C | T | N | O | Y | A | R | A |
| E | D | N | I | R | R | T | E | S | U | L | I | O | T | I |
| E | P | A | O | L | N | E | I | R | O | E | I | S | O | Z |
| A | T | Y | V | E | C | D | J | N | L | R | G | N | M | E |

## 72

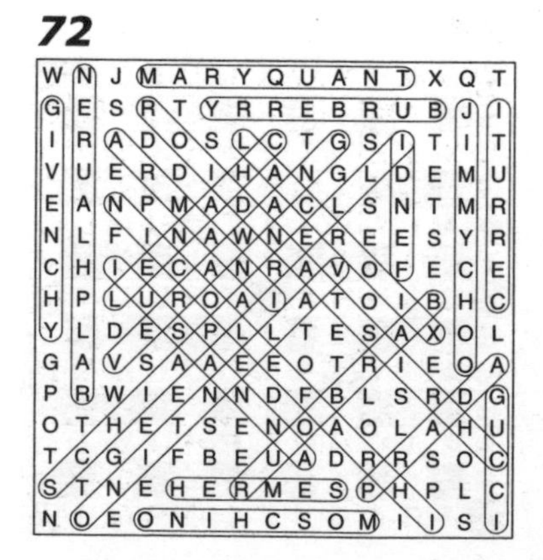

# Solutions

## 74

| | | | | | | | | | | | | | | |
|---|---|---|---|---|---|---|---|---|---|---|---|---|---|---|
| T | S | U | L | R | E | D | N | A | W | M | Y | B | F | J |
| S | Y | M | P | A | T | H | Y | X | S | T | G | C | L | L |
| G | S | C | L | W | B | N | C | A | I | R | L | G | T | F |
| L | A | S | O | O | O | C | I | N | A | J | R | T | A | B |
| L | N | R | E | I | G | S | A | T | Y | O | M | O | Y | R |
| T | R | O | S | N | U | V | I | E | R | Y | I | A | C | W |
| Y | H | N | I | H | L | T | H | N | E | C | L | R | N | A |
| D | E | A | T | S | U | U | O | D | S | V | I | T | E | A |
| T | E | N | P | D | S | A | F | E | I | R | O | E | D | B |
| A | E | S | E | P | N | A | O | R | M | I | L | L | N | O |
| T | N | G | P | X | I | M | P | N | E | F | A | B | O | R |
| E | C | G | I | A | D | N | R | E | H | E | U | I | P | E |
| O | T | E | E | E | I | V | E | S | A | L | H | N | S | D |
| R | T | S | U | R | P | R | I | S | E | E | I | C | E | O |
| Y | A | I | R | O | H | P | U | E | S | O | A | T | D | M |

## 76

| | | | | | | | | | | | | | | |
|---|---|---|---|---|---|---|---|---|---|---|---|---|---|---|
| H | K | N | H | N | G | D | N | P | B | H | I | N | T | D |
| S | A | N | D | A | L | A | O | L | A | C | E | U | P | S |
| R | G | I | N | A | T | L | L | O | S | M | I | L | P | R |
| I | H | A | N | C | F | D | R | O | T | I | A | B | U | G |
| E | R | E | P | P | I | L | S | T | S | N | M | B | M | K |
| L | R | T | I | C | O | U | R | T | S | H | O | E | P | I |
| L | A | L | E | W | H | A | S | N | U | O | E | E | S | R |
| I | F | C | D | R | I | N | T | S | T | A | I | S | E | L |
| R | T | E | N | N | E | A | I | R | E | E | O | K | I | O |
| D | T | W | E | G | O | M | L | S | F | I | A | A | B | A |
| A | B | R | A | E | T | C | E | D | A | E | L | R | N | F |
| P | S | R | G | D | P | H | T | U | N | C | O | L | I | E |
| S | O | O | T | E | E | A | T | S | N | G | C | R | E | R |
| E | L | E | I | O | E | R | O | A | U | T | E | O | C | W |
| C | D | R | G | N | P | M | S | E | L | U | M | I | M | S |

## 78

| | | | | | | | | | | | | | | |
|---|---|---|---|---|---|---|---|---|---|---|---|---|---|---|
| I | J | S | W | E | E | T | S | I | S | K | C | O | S | F |
| I | S | R | E | H | C | U | O | V | I | I | G | R | N | L |
| I | N | B | C | V | T | I | F | T | U | O | W | E | N | O |
| I | N | Y | H | Y | O | G | E | I | N | E | R | P | I | W |
| U | N | R | O | R | T | L | I | C | M | A | B | M | G | E |
| N | R | E | C | T | O | I | G | U | A | A | N | A | Y | R |
| U | R | L | O | A | Y | C | F | M | O | L | L | H | T | S |
| I | T | L | L | E | S | R | H | R | A | C | K | E | N | A |
| R | S | E | A | E | E | O | N | A | O | K | L | C | I | T |
| G | M | W | T | P | S | A | S | H | M | E | E | A | E | T |
| B | E | E | E | E | M | N | O | C | C | P | R | U | H | N |
| S | U | J | S | E | I | L | O | A | A | T | A | E | P | A |
| P | V | O | N | A | L | N | R | K | R | R | E | G | I | L |
| S | R | T | O | A | T | B | Y | E | L | R | F | G | N | P |
| N | M | I | S | B | A | T | H | S | A | L | T | S | A | E |

# Solutions

## 79

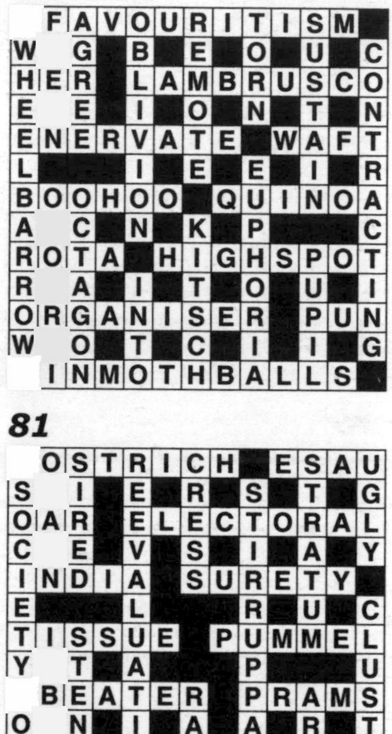

## 80

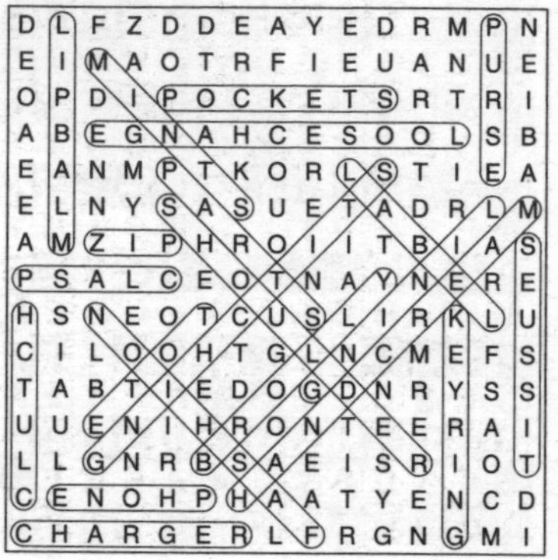

## 81

## 82

| F | V | Q | C | T | H | L | N | M | R | B | T | E | L | N |
|---|---|---|---|---|---|---|---|---|---|---|---|---|---|---|
| E | O | T | S | A | F | I | S | H | E | S | A | L | H | R |
| E | N | O | T | E | P | B | E | L | C | G | U | R | M | E |
| N | E | P | O | T | L | R | F | E | N | B | L | H | C | R |
| T | N | E | S | O | T | A | I | E | A | L | G | S | N | A |
| N | A | M | C | O | T | A | C | C | C | S | A | E | P | E |
| O | W | U | O | A | H | N | E | S | O | G | N | L | A | B |
| I | O | T | R | E | R | A | M | S | I | R | N | I | A | R |
| L | R | I | P | U | E | O | U | T | I | L | N | T | W | E |
| G | E | M | I | F | S | I | T | O | G | R | I | V | S | T |
| S | A | B | O | E | R | A | N | I | N | I | M | E | G | A |
| A | R | H | S | A | R | C | H | E | R | U | C | I | O | W |
| T | E | P | U | I | V | L | N | R | E | S | I | L | S | O |
| A | T | Q | U | E | L | R | G | N | I | M | I | S | E | A |
| H | A | S | E | O | U | T | R | P | N | E | A | B | I | O |

## 83

## 84

| Y | S | K | U | S | M | F | O | R | O | L | R | U | N | F |
|---|---|---|---|---|---|---|---|---|---|---|---|---|---|---|
| O | Y | N | D | C | A | L | R | M | N | A | O | R | I | L |
| L | H | U | O | D | S | T | E | K | C | O | P | S | R | A |
| U | T | E | E | T | A | S | N | O | S | C | T | R | E | R |
| S | D | D | S | I | T | A | T | M | L | O | N | M | N | E |
| P | R | K | O | A | R | U | A | I | N | I | G | A | G | S |
| W | A | H | N | Y | E | E | B | E | T | E | S | U | I | E |
| C | I | T | L | R | S | R | W | A | L | C | T | G | S | O |
| D | N | I | C | E | N | A | C | T | A | I | H | R | E | E |
| E | P | O | I | H | S | L | O | G | G | M | F | I | D | L |
| P | I | A | B | H | E | O | E | H | T | L | E | B | N | C |
| P | P | N | E | R | B | S | T | H | U | A | I | O | T | G |
| I | E | D | E | A | W | A | I | S | T | B | A | N | D | L |
| R | F | R | A | Y | E | D | N | R | E | E | I | O | A | T |
| Y | M | I | N | E | D | E | C | L | R | L | G | N | M | I |

# Solutions

## 85

## 86

H W V Q H S P D S G H T U E I
S O D O E M A C R O E I P C S
O A T A M U L E T L R I C A H
U R E E S O D R K D T I H L L
S A K D A O R N B S T C O K I
E I C I P R A M I A O W K C H
M T O A N U R L U O N E E E D
L E L M S R V I R N A G R N B
O I G A T E E B N N I A L R R
S E O N R I L T T G G T A E M
B A B T N I U Q E S S C A E D
N E R E H S U I O N E T E L P
V A A N W O R C L L G N R E P
P E N D A N T I E S O I A T E
C D L R S G N T M I S A S H E

## 87

| | | | | | | | | | | | | |
|---|---|---|---|---|---|---|---|---|---|---|---|---|
| O | | A | | M | | | | I | | L | | S |
| B | O | U | D | O | I | R | | M | O | I | S | T |
| S | | T | | O | | E | | P | | L | | A |
| C | H | U | R | N | | S | O | L | D | O | U | T |
| U | | M | | | | E | | I | | | | E |
| R | U | N | | M | O | R | O | C | C | A | N | |
| E | | A | | I | | V | | I | | P | | H |
| | C | L | A | S | S | A | C | T | | P | E | A |
| E | | | | T | | T | | | | L | | P |
| B | A | C | A | R | D | I | | S | K | I | M | P |
| O | | O | | U | | O | | U | | Q | | I |
| N | U | D | E | S | | N | U | R | T | U | R | E |
| Y | | E | | T | | | | F | | E | | R |

## 88

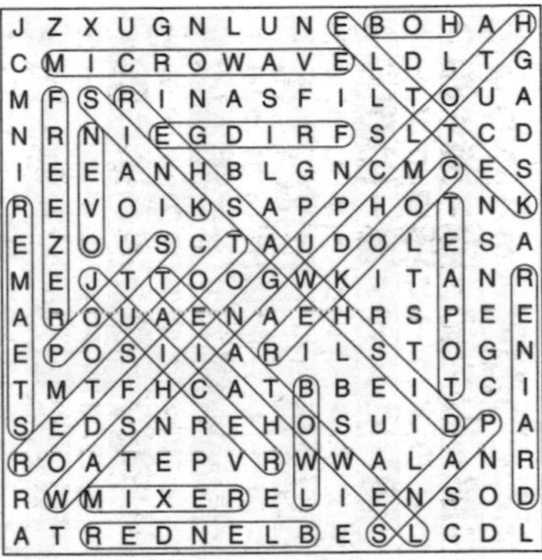

## 89

## 90

C Y V T A O A P A P R I K A T
H R M E R E M M I H S F F E G
E R T U N E E C W R R A L D O
S E T N L E P O O I H A A U N
T H E O E L L S V R C T M N N
N C I A B G E O I E A L E W G
U N S O Y B L D T H I L A A Y
T E P S U O H U W N W D E C R
D L O D U S A O D I K I T A R
E R N S A S E O I N N L T N E
R U B Y M I S T I G I E F G B
K A B L E C D P M I R A G E N
N S U R E S O R T F O S H L A
S S U I O T E P V A L N R I R
T E I D S O A T Y E C D L C C

# Solutions

## 91

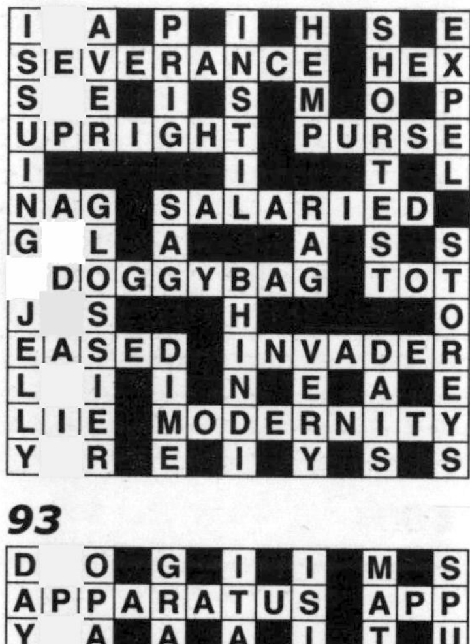

## 92

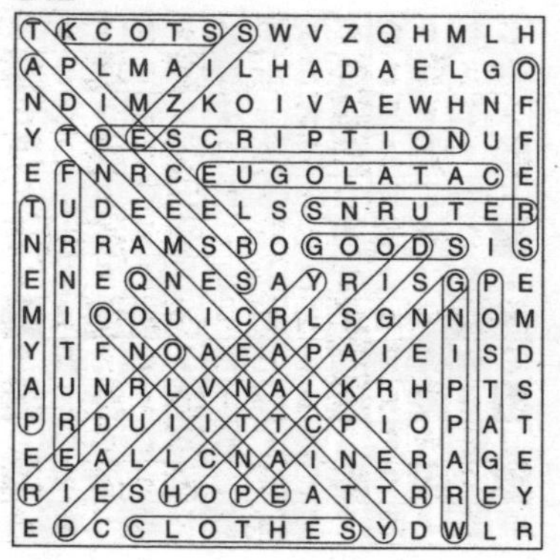

## 93

| | | | | | | | | | | | | |
|---|---|---|---|---|---|---|---|---|---|---|---|---|
| D | | O | ■ | G | ■ | I | ■ | I | ■ | M | ■ | S |
| A | P | P | A | R | A | T | U | S | ■ | A | P | P |
| Y | | A | ■ | A | ■ | A | ■ | I | ■ | T | ■ | U |
| C | O | L | O | N | E | L | ■ | S | N | E | E | R |
| A | ■ | ■ | ■ | ■ | ■ | I | ■ | ■ | ■ | R | ■ | S |
| R | E | D | ■ | D | U | C | K | P | O | N | D | ■ |
| E | | O | ■ | O | ■ | ■ | ■ | A | ■ | A | ■ | B |
| ■ | I | L | L | T | I | M | E | D | ■ | L | E | O |
| L | | P | ■ | ■ | ■ | I | ■ | ■ | ■ | ■ | ■ | R |
| E | T | H | O | S | ■ | D | E | V | O | L | V | E |
| M | | I | ■ | I | ■ | W | ■ | E | ■ | O | ■ | D |
| O | W | N | ■ | L | E | A | V | I | N | G | D | O |
| N | | S | ■ | K | ■ | Y | ■ | L | ■ | O | ■ | M |

## 94

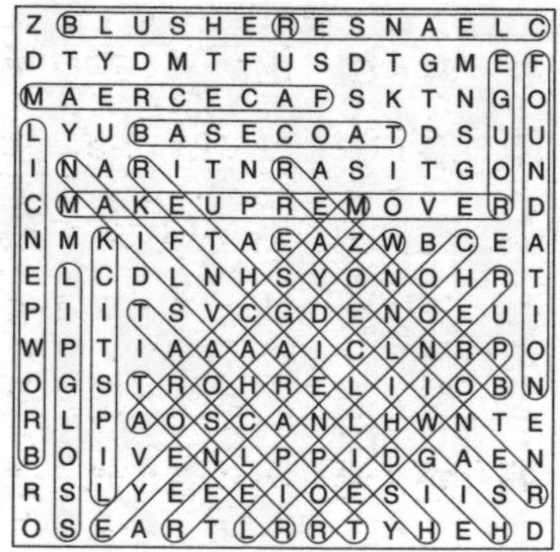

## 95

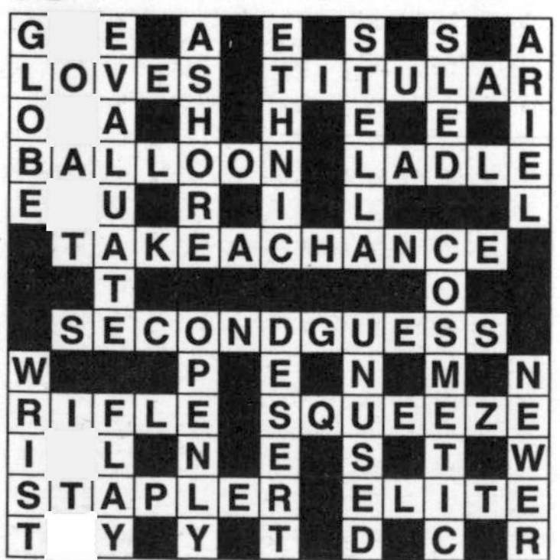

## 96

D D U D G D Z M A R B L E D D
E O E H I U E G S N M S O M E
N N S R O A P O H P P U N O L
I S O D U G L A O A O M I T P
L S N E S G O P T T F T I T P
H T U D N S I C O T T C T L A
R I I N G N H F D B E A M E D
S P O A R Y P E R Y I R T D D
A P H B N I L I E Y U C N S R
A L O I E K N L N A R S O E I
L E G B C D S D E P I R T S D
M D A E L I F A B D E Z A R C
E L R E A C C H E C K E R E D
D F D P T T A R T A N N R H S
U I Y K A E R T S O E A L N R

# Solutions

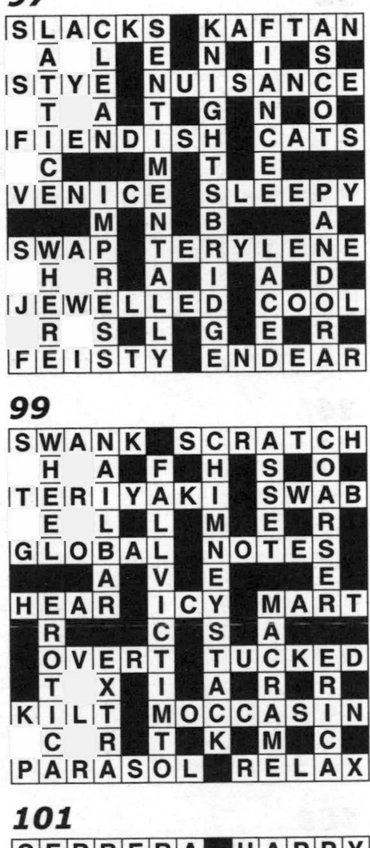

## 98

```
W A U Q S G Y G O P Q U E E N
F O O W S S E H C U D S C Y L
G E I P W S O T M F S O L S H
A F M O O C E O T E U I A S A
E R M A B S T R N N L G E E U
N A R O L H T O T L R M T R N
N U E I E E R E A C A S P T T
H L T R N A S S W D A D S I I
Y E S C B S L R S A A O Y A E
I I I D A U G H T E R T E W L
M N S S N A R O I B C D C L E
A R E T S N I P S E T N E D G
I F A B C I D N R L H I I S O
D T P A L N M R I L O R N R S
A H E R O I N E T E B Y E C P
```

## 100

```
F O A L T E L G A E M F D J Y
Q L T S S S N M S D A U C E A
N S A O A R H N S R C O O U A
D R D M M I N E R K H J A S B
O R P G B I N O L F I L L Y E
W H O U N E W I A N C S T R C
E H L O T I N D R I K A E O E
N M E T S G L O L R T V L I A
E H I L N R U S R E L T G E C
D K I D P E S F O E V R I A O
P Y B A B F I R T G T E P E N
U N A F R I S Y E O I T R T M
P A W L E E B A U Q S C I E D
P N R A H H S U I O T E V L T
Y A N C F R C Y G N E T E I S
```

## 101

## 102

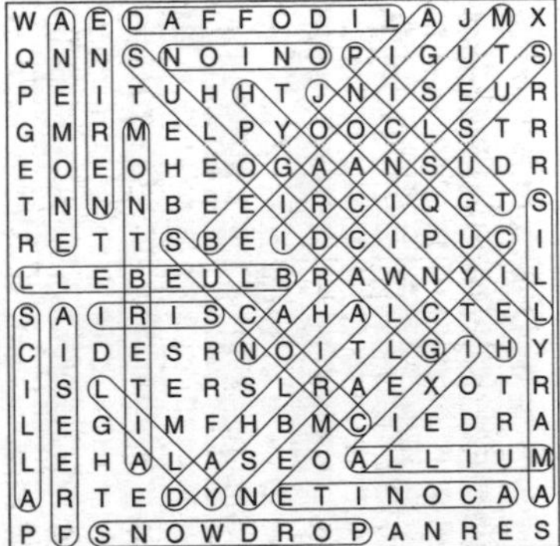

# Solutions

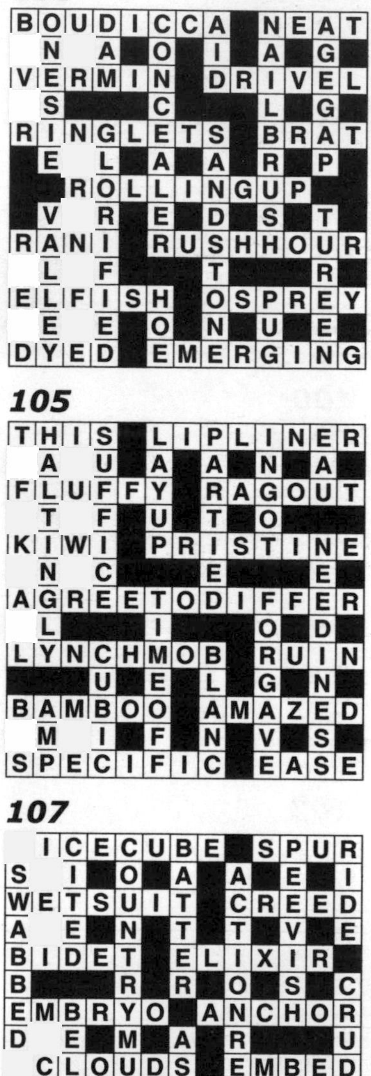

## 104

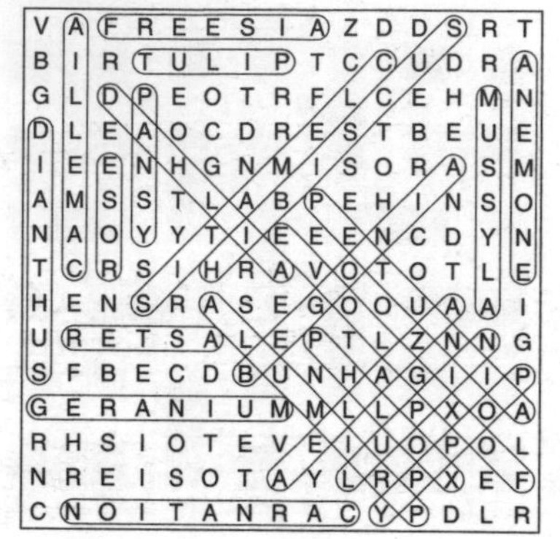

## 106

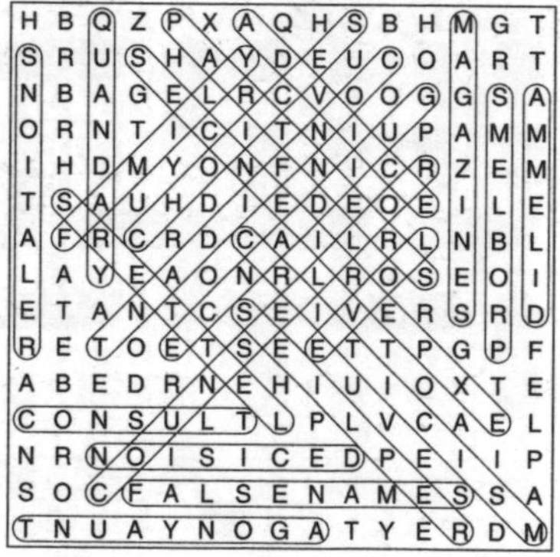

## 108

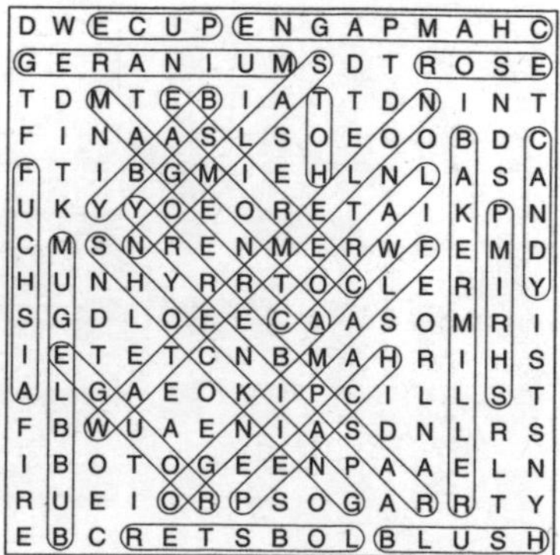